FIELD GUIDE TO
AMPHIBIANS AND REPTILES
OF
SOUTH DAKOTA

By

Alyssa M. Kiesow

Front cover photo: Painted Turtles - Doug Backlund
Back cover photo: Prairie Rattlesnake - Doug Backlund
Line illustrations - Kristie Lovett

South Dakota Department of Game, Fish and Parks
Pierre, South Dakota

SERVING PEOPLE, MANAGING WILDLIFE
Division of Wildlife Mission Motto

FIELD GUIDE TO
AMPHIBIANS AND REPTILES

OF

SOUTH DAKOTA

Copyright © 2006 by South Dakota Department of Game, Fish and Parks

Published by South Dakota Department of Game, Fish and Parks
523 E. Capitol Avenue
Pierre, SD 57501

The publication of this book was funded in part by the
Wildlife Conservation and Restoration Program.

The compact discs with audio sounds of anurans in South Dakota were funded
by the South Dakota Parks and Wildlife Foundation.

Library of Congress Control Number: 2006939286
ISBN 0-9712463-3-5

PREFACE

"These foul and loathsome animals are abhorrent because of their cold body, pale color, cartilaginous skeleton, filthy skin, fierce aspect, calculating eye, offensive smell, harsh voice, squalid habitation, and terrible venom; and so their Creator has not exerted His powers to make many of them."
Carl Linnaeus, 1758

As is obvious from the above quotation, the Scandinavian biologist Carl Linnaeus had a less than favorable opinion of reptiles and amphibians. Most modern biologists, however, have a much different opinion. Herpetologists, biologists who study reptiles and amphibians, find this group of animals fascinating. More than 5,300 species of amphibians and 8,000 species of reptiles have been described.

Reptiles and amphibians, otherwise known as herpetofauna, or herps for short, occur on every continent except Antarctica. Unfortunately, they have been experiencing global declines for the last few decades. Scientists studying this decline have identified a number of possible causative factors: introduced diseases, climate change, ultraviolet (UV) exposure due to ozone depletion, habitat destruction and modification, pesticide and herbicide use, invasive species, parasitic infections, harvesting pressures, and persecution by humans. Habitat factors are usually cited as the greatest threats to reptilian and amphibian populations, although diseases such as chytridiomycosis are thought to be very important in causing the declines. Studies have shown that it is probably a combination of factors causing declines in a particular area. In addition to global declines, amphibians have also been found in the last decade with increased levels of deformities such as missing or extra legs and eyes. The cause of these deformities is poorly known and controversial at this time.

Sadly, reptiles and amphibians are among the most misunderstood of all creatures. They are often viewed as a disposable part of the animal kingdom. Public sympathy for conservation of rare birds or mammals rarely extends to herps. However, reptiles and amphibians play important ecological roles and are increasingly important in the field of medicine. Many are excellent predators on pests such as insects and rodents. Because most amphibians depend on clean water, they serve as environmental indicators of wetland health. Research on freeze tolerance of some amphibians has the potential to extend the viability of transplant organs. Many reptiles and amphibians are of interest in pharmacological studies. Recent studies have used amphibians as models to test opioid agonists, which activate receptors producing analgesia, or the loss of pain without loss of consciousness. In addition, amphibian skin has provided the source for numerous powerful painkillers and antimicrobial compounds.

We hope this book will help to change the undeserved poor opinion many have of reptiles and amphibians. They need all the exposure they can get.

Jody C. Hibma, MS
University of South Dakota

ACKNOWLEDGEMENTS

The South Dakota Department of Game, Fish and Parks would like to acknowledge the efforts of several individuals in the development of this book. Eileen Dowd Stukel, Doug Backlund, and Brenda Boyle played integral roles in the development of this field guide, and their assistance is much appreciated. Other South Dakota Department of Game, Fish and Parks personnel, including Steve Thompson, Nora Kohlenberg, and Michael Lees, also contributed to this field guide, as did Wayne Winter of the South Dakota Parks and Wildlife Foundation.

Many individuals reviewed a draft of this field guide, providing comments and suggestions to better this publication. Those individuals included Dr. David Swanson and Jody Hibma (University of South Dakota); Doug Backlund, Eileen Dowd Stukel, Dana Hess, Chuck Schlueter, Chad Tussing, and Steve Thompson (South Dakota Department of Game, Fish, and Parks); Dr. Brian Smith (Black Hills State University); and Josh Kiesow (Lower Brule Sioux Tribe).

Kristie Lovett completed the illustrations in this book. Kristie would like to thank Doug Backlund, Sarah Bandas, Suzanne L. Collins, and John Sullivan for allowing her to use their photographs as reference photos for her illustrations. Herpetologists and photographers who allowed use of photographs are given credit by each contributed photo. Brenda Boyle completed the layout, and her efforts are much appreciated.

This publication was funded by an allocation to the South Dakota Department of Game, Fish and Parks from the Wildlife Conservation and Restoration Program. These federal funds were administered by the United States Fish and Wildlife Service and matched by the South Dakota Department of Game, Fish and Parks. The South Dakota Parks and Wildlife Foundation donated funds to purchase the audio compact discs supplied with this field guide.

TABLE OF CONTENTS

Mosquitoes feeding on Northern Leopard Frog   Doug Backlund

INTRODUCTION TO AMPHIBIANS AND REPTILES

Amphibians (Class Amphibia) and reptiles (Class Reptilia) are two major classes of vertebrates. Most herpetofauna, also called herps, are harmless to people, and only one South Dakota species, the prairie rattlesnake, is venomous. Herps are rather sedentary and do not travel or migrate long distances, as do other vertebrates such as birds and mammals, although herps can move many miles during their active season.

Amphibians and reptiles rely on the environment and on their behavior to regulate body temperature. This type of thermoregulation is called ectothermy. Cold blooded is not the best term to describe their habits, since many herps, particularly reptiles, maintain a relatively high body temperature. In fact, their body temperatures may exceed those of the environment. Herps are typically active on warm days and sluggish on cool days; extreme hot or cold temperatures can be fatal. Some herps sit or bask on warm surfaces in the heat of the sun to warm themselves.

Herps must hibernate to survive cold, harsh winters in temperate areas. During hibernation, herps may bury themselves in the mud under water or beneath the frost line on dry land. Some have evolved a freeze-tolerant strategy to avoid cell destruction during cold winter periods, allowing them to winter above the frost line.

Amphibians date to the Devonian Period, approximately 360 to 400 million years ago. They have moist, glandular skin, although some, such as toads, can withstand dry conditions. Amphibians produce soft, jellylike eggs, which dehydrate easily. As a result, many amphibians are closely tied to water, and all amphibians found in South Dakota must return to water to lay their eggs. Amphibians experience two life stages - larval and adult. Eggs hatch into larvae with gills. Frog and toad larvae are called tadpoles. Salamander larvae have no special name. Tadpoles become adults with lungs. Adults can emerge from the water, although some amphibians remain completely aquatic. Amphibians include salamanders and newts, frogs and toads (anurans), and caecilians. South Dakota has 15 known species of frogs, toads, and salamanders. No newts or caecilians are found in South Dakota.

Reptiles date to the Pennsylvanian Period, approximately 300 million years ago. Because of their scaled bodies and hard-shelled eggs, reptiles do not depend on water, except for ordinary physiological processes. As a result, reptiles can exploit most terrestrial habitats. Reptiles breathe using lungs and lay eggs on land. They have no larval period. Some retain eggs internally until they hatch, giving birth to "live" young enclosed in a thin transparent membrane. Some even have a quasiplacental attachment, although it is not as sophisticated as is found in mammals. Reptiles include crocodiles, turtles, lizards, snakes, and the tuatara. South Dakota has 31 known reptile species.

This book covers all herpetofauna found in South Dakota. Most species accounts are written using data collected in South Dakota. In some cases, the life history of species that are poorly known in South Dakota is described using information from elsewhere. This book also includes information on museum specimens for amphibians and reptiles in South Dakota (Appendix A), species checklists (Appendix B) and keys (Appendix C) to identify species in South Dakota. Keys are provided to identify adults only, with the exception of salamanders. Larvae or tadpoles are difficult to identify to genus or species without special training.

A BRIEF HISTORY OF THE STUDY OF AMPHIBIANS
AND REPTILES IN SOUTH DAKOTA

Amphibians and reptiles in South Dakota have not received much attention through the years. Early studies emphasized basic survey work. For example, Over (1923, 1943) completed a checklist for South Dakotan amphibians and reptiles. Fishbeck and Underhill (1959) conducted similar studies, but they also collected reference specimens.

Dr. D. G. Dunlap, of the University of South Dakota, was a herpetologist for many years (Dunlap 1967). Some specimens collected during his survey work were placed in the University of South Dakota Museum. This museum no longer maintains amphibian and reptile specimens, and these specimens are now housed at the University of Nebraska State Museum.

Since these basic surveys, studies in South Dakota have ranged widely in their focus. Darrow (1961) researched food habits of the western painted turtle and snapping turtle in southeastern South Dakota. Timken (1968) collected data on turtles throughout South Dakota. Hammer (1968) researched the life history of snapping turtles at LaCreek National Wildlife Refuge. Hardy (1972) examined northern leopard frog population dynamics, while DelFosse (1973) focused on herpetofauna distribution in South Dakota and developed an identification key. Peterson (1974) surveyed the Black Hills for amphibians and reptiles. Nearly a decade later, Kirsch (1983) researched eastern hog-nosed snakes. More recently, Flowers (1994) conducted research on Great Plains and Woodhouse's toads in southeastern South Dakota. Fischer (1998) surveyed the amphibians of eastern South Dakota and developed a field guide (Fischer et al. 1999).

Harris (1935) examined the development of bullsnake embryos, and Johnson (1935) looked at the anatomy of the digestive and urogenital systems of the horned toad. Anderson (1964) studied the growth of the anterior lobe of the pituitary gland of *Rana pipiens* larvae, and Nelson (1965) focused on the thyroid and neurohypophysis in the leopard frog. Kruse (1973) looked at the two morphotypes of *Rana pipiens*, Schramm (1977) looked at taurine synthesis in dog and frog hearts, and Niebel (1979) examined taurine synthesis in frog hearts. Fenwick (1981) focused on spermatogenesis of *Rana pipiens*, *Rana blairi*, and their hybrids. Edwards (1999) looked at cryoprotectant synthesis in freeze-tolerant chorus frogs. Carr (2000) focused on the localization of glutamate receptor subunits in the brain stem and cerebellum of *Chrysemys picta*, and Jenkins (2000) studied the bioenergetics of freeze thaw cycles in chorus frogs. Ernst (2001) investigated the *Rana pipiens* complex in southwestern South Dakota. Other studies relevant to South Dakota herps include Smith (1963), Smith et al. (1966), Timken (1969), and Wilmot et al. (2001).

More recent surveys for herps began in the late 1990s. Hays and Hays (1999) surveyed the southeastern region, Hibma and Hibma (2001) the south central region, Olson (2001) the south central region, Wilmot et al. (2001) the southeastern region, Jessen (2002, 2003) the eastern region, and Fogell (2003) and Fogell and Cunningham (2005) the southeastern region. Bandas (2003) investigated the distribution of turtles in South Dakota. Additional surveys include those conducted in the Black Hills of South Dakota from 1997–2004 (Smith et al. 2004). South Dakota Game, Fish and Parks funded statewide herpetofaunal surveys in 2004, which are summarized in Backlund (2005). These surveys provided information on herpetofauna distributions in South Dakota.

HABITAT IN SOUTH DAKOTA

South Dakota's approximately 75,956 square miles (122,213 sq. km) of diverse habitats include tallgrass prairie in the east and mixed-grass prairie and the Black Hills in the west. The western and eastern portions of South Dakota are divided by the Missouri River. The area east of the Missouri River is known as "east river," and the area west of the Missouri River is called "west river." East river was glaciated and contains tallgrass prairies and glacial prairie potholes, particularly in the northeastern portion. Several major rivers, the James, Vermillion, and Big Sioux, flow north to south. West river was unglaciated, although there are glacial relicts along the Missouri River. West river features several major rivers, such as the Cheyenne, White, and Grand, that flow west to east within the predominant mixed-grass prairie. The Black Hills are located on the western border of the state. Topographic relief ranges from 960 feet (293 m) along the Minnesota River in northeastern South Dakota to 7,242 feet (2,207 m) at Harney Peak in the Black Hills.

Amphibians and reptiles occur in both aquatic and terrestrial habitats in South Dakota, depending on various climates and habitats. Amphibians generally select moist, cool areas, while reptiles prefer dry, warm areas, except for aquatic turtles. Since South Dakota has a continental semiarid climate, the state has more reptile species than amphibians.

Aquatic habitats include pothole wetlands, coulees, backwater areas, oxbow lakes, and streams. Wetlands may be temporary, seasonal, semipermanent, or permanent. Streams range from small creeks to large rivers.

Stratford Slough in northeastern South Dakota   Dave Ode

A prairie pothole in eastern South Dakota   Dave Ode

White River in western South Dakota   Dave Ode

Backwater area in southeastern South Dakota   Sam Stukel

Missouri River in southeastern South Dakota   Sam Stukel

Terrestrial habitats include open prairies, forests, sandhill and sagebrush areas, and prairie dog towns. Tallgrass prairie is found in the easternmost portion of the state, with mixed-grass prairie predominating elsewhere. Forests include deciduous, coniferous, and woody draws along riparian areas.

Sandhills in south central South Dakota   Dave Ode

Tallgrass prairie in northeastern South Dakota   Dennis Skadsen

RARE AMPHIBIANS AND REPTILES

No amphibian or reptile species in South Dakota is currently listed as federally threatened or endangered. The South Dakota Game, Fish and Parks Commission has the authority to modify the state list of threatened or endangered species. At present, this list includes three reptile species. The false map turtle (*Graptemys pseudogeographica*) and eastern hog-nosed snake (*Heterodon platirhinos*) are state threatened, and the lined snake (*Tropidoclonion lineatum*) is a state endangered species.

Many rare herps in South Dakota are granted legal protection through state rules that prevent commercial and noncommercial harvest. The South Dakota Natural Heritage Program (SDNHP) monitors rare species and unique habitats. Biological information is collected and recorded in the South Dakota Natural Heritage Database (SDNHD). The database helps to guide inventory, monitoring, and conservation activities.

The Wildlife Diversity Program's Website has more information about rare or protected herps at http://www.sdgfp.info/Wildlife/Diversity/index.htm.

Short-horned Lizard   Doug Backlund

THREATS TO AND CONSERVATION OF AMPHIBIANS AND REPTILES

Amphibians and reptiles are declining worldwide due to habitat loss and degradation, diseases, introduced and invasive species, environmental pollution, climate change, UV exposure due to ozone depletion, pesticide and herbicide use, harvesting pressures, and persecution by humans. Important herp habitats are declining rapidly. Of most importance is loss and degradation of wetlands and riparian areas. River systems are manipulated with dams and other structures that alter the natural flow and reduce islands and sandbars in the river, which are important turtle nesting areas. Introduced or invasive species may outcompete and prey on native species. For example, bullfrogs are native to south central South Dakota, but have been introduced widely into southeastern South Dakota. These large frogs are notoriously voracious eaters, often eating smaller frogs. As bullfrogs expand in southeastern South Dakota, rare frogs such as northern cricket frogs may be eaten or displaced.

Stocking of fish in normally fishless wetlands, such as temporary and semipermanent wetlands, can be detrimental to amphibians. Some amphibian species depend on fish-free wetlands as breeding habitat. Eggs and larvae of these species are vulnerable to heavy predation from fish.

Pollution may lead to population declines and malformations in herps, particularly amphibians. Amphibians are sometimes considered indicators of environmental quality because of their high sensitivity to pollution. The semipermeable skin of many amphibians may allow pollutants to readily enter their bodies.

Much is unknown about the status of South Dakotan herp populations, such as whether they are declining, increasing, or stable. This presents an opportunity for cooperation to help herps by maintaining suitable habitat for amphibians and reptiles, improving water quality, and reducing species introductions in South Dakota to protect native species. Because herps are important to our ecosystems, we should work together to conserve these species.

Deformed (three-legged)   Aaron Gregor
Leopard Frog

FINDING AND OBSERVING AMPHIBIANS AND REPTILES

Several methods may be used to survey herpetofauna. Techniques include road surveys by vehicle, night surveys with flashlights, daytime visual surveys, frog or toad calling surveys, and surveys by seining aquatic habitats. Heyer et al. (1994) described standard techniques for surveying amphibians. Karns (1986) also described herpetofauna survey techniques, which are used by many local "herpers." In addition, ASIH (2004) designed the "Guidelines for Use of Live Amphibians and Reptiles in Field Research." The Wisconsin Department of Natural Resources has enlisted volunteers since 1984 in a project to survey frogs and toads in the state.

Road surveys are effective for some species. Some herps are attracted to the heat provided by the road surface, and they are easy to see in this open setting. The best search time varies with species. Road surveys can also reveal dead herpetofauna along roads or in ditches. Road surveys entail driving slowly while observing roadsides and ditches.

Herpetofauna that feed at night are detectable during night surveys, which are best conducted in likely herp habitats, such as ponds, streams, woodlots, or shelterbelts or in areas where amphibians are calling. Night surveys involve walking through various habitats while shining a flashlight to locate the calling amphibian for identification purposes or listening for frog and toad calls and recording or identifying the species by the call.

One of the best methods to find herps is by observation in likely habitats, including areas near water, woodlots, old farmsteads, and sandhills. Rocks, flat pieces of plywood and other trash, and logs can be turned over to find herps hiding beneath them. Return the cover object to its original location, since these items provide habitat for many organisms, including herps. Seining ponds or streams can be effective in collecting certain species.

Some specimens may need to be captured to positively identify them. Frogs, toads, and salamanders are easy to capture and handle by grasping them by hand. Wear gloves to avoid contact with their skin, since these species release secretions that can irritate a person's mucous membranes. Lizards are fast and agile, making them difficult to capture and handle. A stealthy approach might work, and the use of nooses may help in capturing lizards.

Except for the prairie rattlesnake, all snakes found in South Dakota are nonvenomous, although some may deliver painful bites. The venomous prairie rattlesnake should be treated with caution if encountered while surveying. Only trained individuals should handle prairie rattlesnakes.

When handling herpetofauna, be careful to prevent injuries to yourself and the animal, which can be harmed with improper handling. Grasp small amphibians and lizards by placing the thumb and forefinger on the hind leg, allowing the animal's body to rest on your hand. They may thrash around so consider grasping the abdomen instead. Grasp large amphibians around the abdomen with the hind legs extended. Hold large snakes with two hands to avoid causing a thrashing snake to injure itself. Place one hand near the head and another farther down the body. Hold snapping turtles by the hind legs or back edge of the shell. Make sure the head is always pointed away from your body, since they can deliver a very strong and sometimes dangerous bite. Holding a snapping turtle only by the tail may permanently injure its spinal cord. Hold softshell turtles near the back edge of their shell. Other South Dakota turtles may be handled by grasping their shells through the midsection. After identifying the animal, release it where it was captured.

Cover boards attract herps that seek shelter beneath them.

Aaron Gregor

HOW TO USE THIS FIELD GUIDE

This guide is designed to help the reader identify species and understand habitat needs and life history attributes of amphibians and reptiles found in South Dakota. Citations are generally not included in the text for ease of reading, but a *References* section credits sources used in preparing this document.

To identify an unknown amphibian and reptile, first refer to the dichotomous keys and individual photographs. The maps and species accounts will further aid in identification. The maps show general distributions of herps in South Dakota, and the species accounts detail the natural history of each species. Some species are difficult to identify. In these cases, take photographs, record the exact location, and seek help from a biologist or herpetologist.

Photographs depict each species' adult form and sometimes the young or juvenile. Distribution maps were created using several sources: Fishbeck and Underhill (1959), Timken (1968), Thompson (1976), Fischer et al. (1999), Thompson and Backlund (1999), Ballinger et al. (2000), Perkins and Backlund (2000), SDNHP (2006), Jessen (2002, 2003), Bandas (2003), Fogell (2003), Fogell and Cunningham (2005), and Backlund (2005). Each map shows the probable distribution based on sightings and habitat.

Species accounts begin by listing the scientific and common names of the species as given by NatureServe (2006) and Frost et al. (2006). Frog and toad names are based on Frost et al. 2006. All other names follow those of NatureServe (2006). The species names in this book may differ from those in other sources because of findings from genetics studies and other investigations into how species and genera are related to each other. In fact, name changes are likely to continue as a result of new investigations. A genus or species name may be abbreviated to the first letter only the second time it is used within a species account. When a new order or family begins, the guide contains a brief description of that order or family.

Size, appearance, and distinguishing characteristics are listed in the *Physical Characteristics* section. The *Habitat and Habits* section includes common habitats for each species and various behavioral characteristics. Information on habitats and habits of a species that is specific for South Dakota is described if such information is available. Taxonomy refers to a listing of subspecies of a particular species found in South Dakota. Distribution describes the range of each species in the United States and in South Dakota. Status describes the legal protection by state or federal law and the species' rarity. These three topics are covered in the *Taxonomy/Distribution and Status* section. The *Remarks* section includes other interesting information about the species. Some species accounts contain a *Special References* section that lists pertinent literature for the species.

AMPHIBIANS

Amphibians include frogs, toads, salamanders, newts, and caecilians. Approximately 5,300 amphibian species are found worldwide, and new species and genera are discovered each year. At present, more than 160 species of amphibians exist in North America. South Dakota has two orders, six families, eight genera, and 15 species of amphibians. Orders found within the state are the Caudata (salamanders) and Anura (frogs and toads).

Amphibians do not have claws on their feet, although arboreal frogs may have toe pads for climbing, and burrowing toads may have spurs on the hind feet for digging or burrowing. Amphibians have moist, glandularized skin, although toads have dry skin. The skin of aquatic frogs is highly permeable to allow gas exchange in aquatic environments. Toads have parotid glands just behind the head. These glands release a toxin to deter predators by irritating their mouths. The toxin can be dangerous to some vertebrates, especially dogs. Treefrogs can change color depending on the ambient temperature and their physical state, such as during breeding.

Although some amphibians range far from water, most depend on water for survival. All South Dakota amphibians must lay eggs in water for successful reproduction. The amphibian life cycle starts with eggs, which are deposited and fertilized in aquatic environments. Eggs hatch into aquatic larvae, known as tadpoles in the anurans. Aquatic larvae eventually metamorphose to terrestrial adults, a process that takes several weeks to years depending on the species. One exception to this life cycle is the mudpuppy, which lives an exclusively aquatic life. Tiger salamanders normally metamorph to terrestrial adult forms, but under certain conditions, some may lead an entirely aquatic life. Adults that retain gills demonstrate neoteny, which can occur in sexually mature adult tiger salamanders. These adults resemble larvae and have similar habits as larvae.

Amphibian eggs are gelatinous and have a pigmented center, which absorbs sunlight to initiate growth and development. Tadpoles are fully aquatic and breathe using gills. They are difficult to identify, and this book does not include a key for their identification. Frog and toad larvae generally have tails, and salamander larvae typically have legs and tails. In addition, an anuran tadpole and a salamander larvae have different body shapes.

Salamanders have tails and relatively equal-sized legs. Males develop enlarged vents with large tubercles during the breeding season. Compared to frogs and toads, male salamanders have broader fins during their aquatic stage. Unlike salamanders, adult frogs and toads lack tails, and their front legs are smaller than their back legs. Frogs and toads, particularly males, vocalize primarily during the breeding season, when they develop vocal sacs and enlarged thumbs.

Frogs and toads reproduce by external fertilization. Males congregate during the spring in breeding areas, such as ponds, to vocalize and attract females. Each species has its own unique voice. Once females arrive at breeding areas, males compete for them by shoving and pushing to determine dominance. A dominant male grabs a female from behind, a position called amplexus. Eggs are fertilized as they are released. Hundreds to thousands of eggs may be deposited during breeding, depending on the species.

Salamanders reproduce by internal fertilization, but without copulation. In spring or fall, salamanders form breeding aggregations for courtship and egg laying. Males push, rub, and nudge females and eventually release sperm in small packets for females to collect. Females pick up sperm with their cloacal lips and internally fertilize the eggs.

Amphibians play an important role in the ecosystem. They are often herbivorous as larvae and carnivorous as adults, eating insects and other invertebrates. Amphibians are an essential food source for many aquatic and terrestrial animals.

Order Caudata

The order Caudata includes the salamanders and newts. Larvae, juveniles, and adults have tails. The larval form usually metamorphoses into a terrestrial adult. Limbs are perpendicular to the body and are of relatively equal size. Members of this order are carnivorous in all stages of their life cycle, typically preying on invertebrates of various types.

Family Ambystomatidae

The family Ambystomatidae includes the mole salamanders, which are widely distributed throughout most of North America. Although they may be found in many habitat types, individuals often inhabit forested areas having abundant burrows and leaf litter. They typically breed in ponds or slow-moving streams.

TIGER SALAMANDER
Ambystoma tigrinum

Physical Characteristics:

Adult tiger salamanders are 6 to 9 inches (15 to 22 cm) from head to tail. They have five toes on the hind feet; solid, round heads; cylindrical bodies; tiny, protruding eyes; and smooth, moist skin. Many have large faint yellow, olive brown, to black blotches, spots, or bars across the body, which may be colored dark gray or olive. The belly is gray to olive with yellow mottling, and the chin is yellow. Coloration may become more blotched and less spotted with age. Males tend to have longer tails than females, and females tend to have larger bodies, although these characteristics are not reliable to determine sex. Larval tiger salamanders have external gills near the base of the head that appear yellowish green with speckling of dark spots.

The tiger salamander can demonstrate neoteny, where individuals become sexually mature while retaining larval characteristics. These individuals never leave water. They become as large as, or larger than, their terrestrial counterparts. Individuals experiencing this condition can mate and reproduce. Neoteny may occur because of specific environmental conditions, such as low temperature. If these conditions change, individuals can complete metamorphosis and attain normal maturity. Neoteny is also called paedomorphism.

Taxonomy/Distribution and Status:

Two subspecies were once recognized in South Dakota. Three subspecies are now recognized, including the blotched tiger salamander (*A. t. melanostictum*), gray tiger salamander (*A. t. diaboli*), and eastern tiger salamander (*A. t. tigrinum*). Subspecific recognition with these salamanders is somewhat controversial.

Tiger salamanders are found throughout the United States and throughout South Dakota. Blotched tiger salamanders are found in central and western South Dakota, gray tiger salamanders are found in northeastern South Dakota, and east-

16

Blotched Tiger Salamander   Dan Fogell

Eastern Tiger Salamander   Michael Graziano

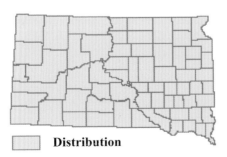

Distribution

17

ern tiger salamanders inhabit southeastern South Dakota.

Habitat and Habits:

Tiger salamanders inhabit moist areas near woodlands, wetlands, and prairies. They may occur in moist areas, such as in basements or root cellars. Individuals seek underground shelter throughout the summer and winter. They are active from April to September. They rest during the day in burrows or under logs, but are active at night, especially after it rains. Tiger salamanders are most active during the warm summer months.

To prepare for the breeding season, adults move to ponds during warm spring rains for courtship and egg deposition. Courtship can be quite elaborate and involve aggressiveness by males and females. They rub their bodies together, thrash their tails, and nip each other. The male moves away from the female after courtship. She follows him, awaiting the deposition of his spermatophore onto the bottom of the pond.

To fertilize her eggs, the female immediately takes up the recently deposited spermatophore with her exposed cloaca, although many spermatophores are missed in this process. She then deposits up to 1,000 eggs in areas where submerged objects, such as leaves or twigs, are available for egg attachment, usually near the bottom of a pond. After a few weeks in early spring, eggs hatch into larvae, which grow throughout the summer.

Larvae typically inhabit springs and ponds. They grow into a terrestrial subadult by July, August, or September, depending on elevation and weather. They become sexually mature the following spring.

Larvae eat a variety of animal prey, such as insects and small fish, while adults eat earthworms, spiders, and small mammals.

Remarks:

Larval tiger salamanders are often sold as fishing bait or in pet stores. They are often mistaken for mudpuppies, and the name mudpuppy is often used for both species. The two species are somewhat similar in appearance, but tiger salamanders have five toes on their hind feet, and mudpuppies have four toes on their hind feet. Tiger salamanders have been widely introduced to new sites by anglers and pet owners. They can discharge a bitter-tasting, milky slime when they are irritated, although they are otherwise harmless.

Family Proteidae

The family Proteidae includes mudpuppies, also called waterdogs. Mudpuppies have filamentous gills and caudal fins and are aquatic as both larvae and adults. Members of the genus *Necturus* have four digits on each foot.

MUDPUPPY

Necturus maculosus

Physical Characteristics:

Adults are 8 to 13 inches (20 to 33 cm) from head to tail. Adults have external reddish gills and thin, orange-tinted tail fins.

Their gray to rusty brown bodies have blue to black speckling and pale gray bellies that sometimes have brownish-black spotting. A dark stripe extends through the eyes. During the breeding season, males differ from females by having a swollen, crescent-shaped ridge in front of the cloacal opening.

Mudpuppies have four toes on their hind feet, compared to five toes on the hind feet of the larval tiger salamander. Gills vary in size depending on environmental conditions, such as the amount of dissolved oxygen present in the water body. In cold waters with sufficient oxygen content, gills are often small and constricted.

Larval mudpuppies are usually broadly striped across the body. One dark stripe stretches down the center of the back, two yellowish stripes extend along each side of the central stripe, and two dark stripes run along the sides from the gills to the end of the tail. Larval mudpuppies are occasionally gray and unmarked.

Taxonomy/Distribution and Status:

The subspecies found in South Dakota is the common mudpuppy (*N. m. maculosus*). It has the largest range among the three subspecies of mudpuppies in the United States and is found in the east central and the north central United States. This subspecies has been documented historically only in northeastern South Dakota. Any sightings or collections should be documented with a photo and reported to the South Dakota Natural Heritage Program.

Habitat and Habits:

Mudpuppies use permanent water bodies, including rivers, creeks, and ponds. Juveniles use shallow waters or riffles, and adults inhabit deep waters. Animals are active at night, although they can be seen during the day traveling through weed-choked or muddy waters. Mudpuppies are active year-round, with bouts of inactivity while they rest beneath submerged logs or rocks.

Mudpuppies breed in the fall, and eggs are internally fertilized. The female releases 75 to 100 fertilized eggs into the water between April and June of the following year. Eggs are usually released beneath submerged structures that provide a surface for egg attachment. After depositing the eggs, the female guards them

19

until they hatch five to seven weeks later. Mudpuppies are sexually mature at four to six years of age.

Mudpuppies eat small aquatic animals such as fish, fish eggs, insects, worms, crayfish, mollusks, and other amphibians.

Remarks:

Anglers often catch mudpuppies, which put up a great fight. Some anglers consider mudpuppies unpleasant and toxic, but they are harmless. If you accidentally catch a mudpuppy, remove it carefully from the hook and release it unharmed.

Mudpuppy

Michael Graziano

Order Anura
The order Anura includes frogs and toads. Anura means "without a tail," a characteristic of adult frogs and toads. Hopping is their primary means of locomotion. Frogs and toads occur on every continent except Antarctica. Larvae (tadpoles) are usually herbivorous, whereas adults are carnivorous.

Family Bufonidae
The family Bufonidae includes true toads. True toads are the only tailless amphibians with large parotid glands. They also have wartlike structures on their backs. The parotid glands and warty structures release a white viscous poison to deter predators. True toads also have horizontal pupils and often search for prey at night.

AMERICAN TOAD
Anaxyrus americanus

Physical Characteristics:
Dry skin covers a medium-sized body, which measures 2 to 4 inches (5 to 9 cm) from snout to vent. Two kidney-shaped parotid glands lie just behind the eyes. These glands are not directly attached to the cranial ridges, which are separate and extend down the forehead and stretch behind the eyes.

American toads are grayish brown with large brownish-black spots. Each spot encircles one or two red, orange, or brown warts, or skin glands. Warts are also present on the lower leg. A light stripe may run down the center of the back. The belly is yellow with dark gray mottling, particularly on the chest and anterior portion of the abdomen.

During the breeding period, hormones cause males to develop swollen thumbs, foreleg horns, and dark gray throats. Females typically have larger heads and bodies than males.

Taxonomy/Distribution and Status:
American toads were recently reclassified from the genus *Bufo* to *Anaxyrus* based on an analysis of evolutionary relationships of amphibians. The subspecies found in South Dakota is the American toad (*A. a. americanus*). These toads range throughout eastern North America. American toads occur east of the Missouri River in South Dakota, primarily in counties along the eastern border. South Dakota marks the extreme western boundary of the species' range.

Habitat and Habits:
American toads use habitats ranging from wooded areas near the edges of hardwood forests and prairies to suburban properties. Most inhabited areas are moist and near water sources, such as semipermanent wetlands. Small ponds are important habitats, since breeding typically occurs in temporary wetlands or slow, shallow streams that lack fish.

American Toad   Dan Fogell

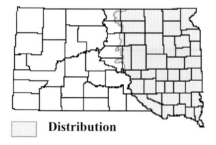

Distribution

22

American toads hide during the day in loose soil under rocks or burrow in depressions beneath the leaf litter. They may use burrows during estivation, the summer equivalent of hibernation, to survive dry spells. American toads search for food at night, with peak activity during warm wet evenings.

American toads individually overwinter by burrowing beneath the frost line (30 to 71 inches deep) into well-drained soils. They are active from late April until October. Calling and breeding last from May to mid-June. Calls are high-pitched extended trills of 20 to 30 seconds with a trill rate of 30 to 40 per second. Breeding occurs when the male mounts the female in the water, a position called amplexus. As the females lay eggs, males release sperm to externally fertilize the discharged eggs. A female releases more than 20,000 eggs in several single-file strings; eggs hatch about one week later. The small, black tadpoles remain in the water until late July, when they transform into toadlets or young toads.

American toads use their long tongues to capture such foods as terrestrial insects and other invertebrates.

Remarks:

The American toad is called the "hoptoad" in the eastern United States. This species hybridizes with Woodhouse's toad (*A. woodhousii*) and the Great Plains toad (*A. cognatus*), but it can be distinguished from hybrids by the presence of large warts on the shanks, spotting on the chest, and separated cranial crests and parotid glands.

The American toad's warts are actually skin glands. Contrary to popular belief, toads cannot transmit warts to humans.

To defend themselves, American toads inflate their bodies, present the parotid glands and its bitter toxin, or urinate on their attacker.

GREAT PLAINS TOAD
Anaxyrus cognatus

Physical Characteristics:

Great Plains toads measure 2 to 4 inches (5 to 9 cm) from snout to vent. The dry, dark tan skin on the back is speckled with many large, irregularly shaped, dark olive dots outlined with light tan. Each spot has multiple warts. Young toads may have small red tubercles mottled across their backs. Great Plains toads have uniformly cream-colored bellies.

This toad has cranial crests on the head, which rise between the eyes and merge on the forward edge just behind the nostrils. These crests produce a "boss" or bulge on their snout, forming a "V" between the eyes. Near the cranial crests are two oval parotid glands, which are less evident in this species than in the American or Canadian toad.

Males have large, elliptical vocal sacs that extend forward above their head when inflated during calling. The onset of the breeding season causes males to begin calling and to develop dark throats and horny foreleg pads. Females are noticeably larger than males.

Taxonomy/Distribution and Status:

Great Plains toads were reclassified into the genus *Anaxyrus* from the *Bufo* genus based on genetic data. No subspecies is identified in South Dakota. Great Plains toads occur in the plains regions of the central United States. This species occurs statewide in South Dakota where suitable habitat exists, with the exception of higher elevations of the Black Hills. Great Plains toads live underground more often during drought conditions, making them appear to be less common than they are.

Habitat and Habits:

Great Plains toads inhabit grasslands and river floodplains. Spring rains and thunderstorms trigger the appearance of Great Plains toads, which immediately move to temporary wetlands and flooded fields to breed. Calls during the breeding season last from late spring through early summer. The breeding call is a series of loud, rapid, chugging sounds that last 20 to 50 seconds, with a trill rate of 13 to 20 sounds per second.

Great Plains toads are active from late April to September or October, although seasonal activity depends on the weather. They are most active at night.

Rainfall determines breeding season length. Females release up to 20,000 eggs. They may release eggs twice per year, weather permitting. Fertilized eggs hatch within one week. Tadpoles become toadlets one month later.

These toads are excellent burrowers, digging to depths of nearly 40 inches to escape the winter cold and summer heat. If conditions become extremely hot and dry, they burrow underground, remaining there through the winter.

Great Plains toads eat terrestrial insects such as ants and beetles.

Great Plains Toad   Dan Fogell

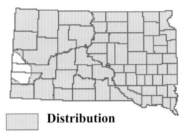

Distribution

Remarks:

American and Woodhouse's toads may hybridize with the Great Plains toad to produce individuals with varying characteristics (see American toad account). The Great Plains toad may defend itself by inflating its body to make it more difficult for predators to swallow it. Great Plains toads historically used old, water-filled buffalo wallows as breeding sites.

Special References:

Flowers, M. A. 1994. Feeding ecology and habitat use of juvenile Great Plains toads (*Bufo cognatus*) and Woodhouse's toads (*B. woodhousei*). M.A. Thesis. University of South Dakota, Vermillion, South Dakota. 79pp.

CANADIAN TOAD
Anaxyrus hemiophrys

Physical Characteristics:

Canadian toads measure 2 to 3 inches (5 to 8 cm) from snout to vent. The dark brown to green skin on the back is speckled with dark spots that have one to two reddish warts per spot. A light mid-dorsal stripe extends down the back. The white belly has gray and black speckling, especially on the throat. This species closely resembles the American toad, but Canadian toads have bosses and large, indistinct, oval parotid glands.

Canadian toads have cranial crests that merge to form a boss on the snout. Young toads develop their crests as they age, and eventually the crests merge to form a boss.

Taxonomy/Distribution and Status:

Canadian toads were reclassified from *Bufo* into *Anaxyrus* based on an extensive phylogenetic study of amphibians. The subspecies found in South Dakota is the Canadian toad (*A. h. hemiophrys*). These toads range into the north central United States, including Montana, North Dakota, South Dakota, and Minnesota. Canadian toads occur in eastern South Dakota.

Habitat and Habits:

Canadian toads are more aquatic than most toad species in South Dakota, frequently occurring near the shores of semipermanent or permanent wetlands. They are good swimmers.

Individuals appear in late April to mid-May, and they are often active during warm summer nights. They emerge to breed in temporary wetlands after late spring or early summer rains. Canadian toads breed during the day throughout June. Breeding calls are soft, low-pitched trills that last two to five seconds and are repeated two or three times a minute. Canadian toad calls are shorter and more rapid than American toad calls. Fertilized eggs hatch as tadpoles several days after they are laid, and toadlets appear by late June or early July.

Canadian toads overwinter near wetlands in social groups. Pocket gopher mounds covered with weedy vegetation, called mima mounds, may be used by aggregations of wintering toads. Canadian toads burrow below the frost line in these overwintering structures.

Canadian toads eat small insects and earthworms.

Remarks:

The Canadian toad is also known as the "Dakota toad." Some scientists consider the American and Canadian toads as subspecies due to the transitional zone where the two species interbreed.

Canadian Toad

Jeffrey B. LeClere

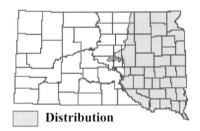

Distribution

Special References:
Breckenridge, W. J., and J. R. Tester. 1961. Growth, local movements and
   hibernation of the Manitoba toad (*Bufo hemiophrys*). Ecology 42:637-646.

27

WOODHOUSE'S TOAD
Anaxyrus woodhousii

Physical Characteristics:

Woodhouse's toads measure 3 to 4 inches (6 to 10 cm) from snout to vent. Their cranial ridges form a high ridge on the forehead and come into contact with elongate parotid glands.

These hefty toads are olive to brown in color. The back has dark brown to green irregular spots with one to six warts per spot. A light, central stripe follows the contours of the back. This characteristic differentiates this toad from the Great Plains toad. Woodhouse's toads have white to pale yellow bellies with no flecking except for an occasional single, dark "breast" spot and/or speckling between the front legs.

During the breeding season, males develop horny pads on the forelegs, a round vocal sac, and a dark throat. Males are generally smaller than females.

Taxonomy/Distribution and Status:

Woodhouse's toads were reclassified into *Anaxyrus* from *Bufo* due to genetic data. The subspecies found in South Dakota is *A. w. woodhousii*. Woodhouse's toad ranges from the Great Plains to the arid Southwest. They are found throughout South Dakota, but are less common in the northeastern region.

Habitat and Habits:

Woodhouse's toads use a variety of habitats such as sandy lowlands, grasslands, backyards, wetlands, and floodplains. They rest in burrows during the day.

Breeding begins in early March and continues through early August, following spring or summer rains. Sites include shallow wetlands, oxbows, or other bodies of water. Based on their calling periods, Woodhouse's toads appear to breed later in the active season and in warmer temperatures than American toads.

Calling begins after males gather near the water's edge. The call lasts one to two and a half seconds. It is a nasal "waaah" and sounds like a loud snore or a bawling calf. Once a female is attracted, she lays up to 25,000 eggs in linear, paired strings. The male fertilizes the eggs when he mounts the female, which is called amplexus. Fertilized eggs hatch in one week as tadpoles that eventually transform into toadlets by late June or mid-July. Woodhouse's toads burrow below the frost line to survive the winter.

Individuals often feed at night near lights, where insects congregate and are easy prey. Prey includes bees, beetles, spiders, and ants.

Remarks:

American and Great Plains toads may hybridize with Woodhouse's toads (see American toad account). Hybridization makes differentiating these species complicated. American and Woodhouse's toads are similar in appearance, although their bellies and cranial crests differ. American toads have flecking on

28

Woodhouse's Toad   Dan Fogell

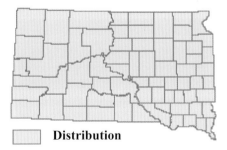

Distribution

29

the belly, and the cranial crests do not touch their parotid glands. Woodhouse's and American toads also have different calls. Canadian and Great Plains toads are also similar to Woodhouse's toad, but Canadian toads have a raised boss between the eyes, which is lacking in Woodhouse's toads. The Woodhouse's toad has a distinctive light line down the center of the back, which is lacking in the Great Plains toad.

The Woodhouse's toad was formerly known as the Rocky Mountain toad. The current name originates from Samuel Washington Woodhouse, a 19th century surgeon and naturalist of southwestern expeditions.

Special References:

Flowers, M. A. 1994. Feeding ecology and habitat use of juvenile Great Plains Toads (*Bufo cognatus*) and Woodhouse's Toads (*B. woodhousei*). M.A. Thesis. University of South Dakota, Vermillion, South Dakota. 79pp.

Family Hylidae

The family Hylidae includes treefrogs, which are small, slender frogs with lean legs. They often have enlarged toe pads due to their arboreal habits, though this depends on the species. Treefrogs have horizontal pupils.

NORTHERN CRICKET FROG
Acris crepitans

Physical Characteristics:

Northern cricket frogs are small robust frogs that are 1 to 2 inches (2 to 4 cm) from snout to vent. The extensively webbed feet lack enlarged toe pads. Green or brown triangles are found between the eyes. The skin is gray to brown and may be mottled with dark blotches. They also have darkly colored warts and dark, indistinct longitudinal stripes on the back. The white belly may have a breast or throat spot. Northern cricket frogs sometimes have a white line from the eye to the base of the foreleg. They may also have irregular lines along the side of the thighs. Males often develop yellow vocal pouches with some speckling during the breeding season.

Taxonomy/Distribution and Status:

No subspecies is designated for this species in South Dakota. Northern cricket frogs occur in the eastern United States, but they may be declining across the northern and western boundaries of their range.

This species was once common across southeastern and south central South Dakota. It is currently considered restricted to the southeastern corner of the state, and populations have disappeared from sites in Tripp and Gregory counties. Due to its rarity in South Dakota, the SDNHP monitors this species.

Habitat and Habits:

This highly aquatic amphibian rarely strays far from water. They use permanent water bodies with emergent vegetation and gently sloping banks.

Northern cricket frogs congregate at water sources, such as roadside ditches and rain pools, to chorus, although chorusing does not necessarily coincide with the breeding season. Their cricketlike calls (or choruses) resemble "gick, gick, gick" echoes, much like striking two stones together. The calls resonate across wetlands at one call per second. Males often call during evenings while gathered in dense clusters on mudflats or in shallow vegetated areas.

Northern cricket frogs breed and call from late May to July. Breeding usually starts with the onset of warm weather and late spring rains. Males attract females by chorusing. Males mount females and fertilize eggs as they are released. Eggs are laid singly or in small masses of 10 to 15 to as many as 200 eggs. Eggs hatch in three to four days as tadpoles with black-tipped tails. Tadpoles become adult frogs in 5 to 10 weeks.

Northern Cricket Frog   Dan Fogell

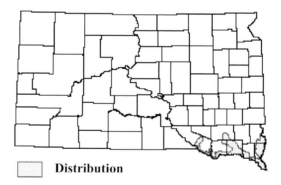

Distribution

Northern cricket frogs survive cold winters by hibernating in terrestrial sites, such as crayfish burrows or cracks in the soil. Individuals are known to hibernate in cracks in the mud. In one study, these cracks were approximately 8 to 10 inches (20 to 25 cm) deep, 1 inch (2.5 cm) wide, and 7 to 10 feet (2 to 3 m) from the edge of a stream. They cannot tolerate freezing temperatures.

Tadpoles eat algae and phytoplankton, and adults eat small insects or spiders.

Remarks:

The Blanchard's cricket frog, once the designated subspecies in South Dakota, was named after Frank Nelson Blanchard, a herpetologist at the University of Michigan.

Special References:

Greenwell, M., V. Beasley, and L. E. Brown. 1996. Mysterious decline of the cricket frog. Aquaticus 26:48-55.

Irwin, J. T., J. P. Costanzo, and R. E. Lee. 1999. Terrestrial hibernation in the northern cricket frog, *Acris crepitans*. Canadian Journal of Zoology 77:1240-1246.

McCallum, M. L., and S. E. Trauth. 2006. An evaluation of the subspecies *Acris crepitans blanchardi* (Anura, Hylidae). Zootaxa 1104:1–21.

COPE'S GRAY TREEFROG
Hyla chrysoscelis

Physical Characteristics:

Cope's gray treefrogs are moderately large when compared to other treefrogs, measuring 1 to 2 inches (3 to 5 cm) from snout to vent. The skin is gray to green in color. Environmental factors and daily activities determine skin color. An individual can change from green to gray, depending on the circumstances. Green is more dominant in warmer temperatures or among green vegetation. They are slightly smaller and greener than gray treefrogs (*Hyla versicolor*). The back is covered with dark blotches, which are more noticeable against the gray skin. These blotches are not bordered in black. The skin has indistinct warts, but is relatively smooth compared to the gray treefrog's skin. This species' inner thighs are yellow, the belly is white to yellow-orange with some gray speckling, and the toes have enlarged pads for tree climbing. Cope's gray treefrogs have large white spots beneath the eyes. During the breeding season, males have dark throats and are lighter in color than females.

Taxonomy/Distribution and Status:

No subspecies is identified in South Dakota. Cope's gray treefrogs inhabit the central and eastern United States. They are restricted to suitable habitat in northeastern and southeastern South Dakota. A small remnant population also exists below the Oahe Dam near Pierre. Due to its rarity in South Dakota, the SDNHP monitors this species.

Habitat and Habits:

Cope's gray treefrogs are found in prairie and forest habitats. They breed in seasonal or semipermanent wetlands. They seek shade during the day in trees or shrubs.

Cope's gray treefrogs are rarely found on or near the ground except during the breeding season, when they are more easily located by their calls. Males begin calling in late May or early June to attract females. Their characteristic metallic call is repeated at a rate of 34 to 69 trills per second. The call rate can be affected by temperature, with cold temperatures resulting in slower than normal call rates.

Males usually call from wetlands or surrounding trees and shrubs. Males mount females in a position called amplexus and fertilize the eggs as they are released. Between 900 and 3,000 eggs are released in clusters of 20 to 90 eggs and fertilized each year. Eggs hatch in four to five days as tadpoles. Tadpoles have high, orange-red tail fins and become froglets within two months.

During the winter, Cope's gray treefrogs hibernate in the soil under ground debris but above the frost line. This species produces plasma glycerol, a natural antifreeze, in the liver to counteract freeze damage to tissues. Individuals may estivate, the summer equivalent of hibernation, if conditions become too dry.

Cope's Gray Treefrog   Doug Backlund

Cope's Gray Treefrog   Jeffrey B. LeClere

Cope's gray treefrogs can change from green to gray, depending on the circumstances.

35

They search for prey, such as insects and spiders, in trees or shrubs near wetlands.

Remarks:

Until 1968, Cope's gray treefrogs and gray treefrogs were considered the same species. Recent research shows that Cope's gray treefrog has 24 chromosomes, and the gray treefrog has 48 chromosomes.

Both Cope's gray treefrogs and gray treefrogs presumably exist in South Dakota. They are difficult to distinguish from one another, so caution must be exercised. Call differences can help distinguish between the two species.

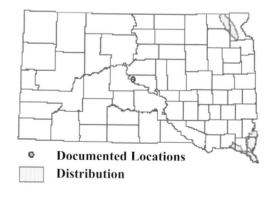

○   **Documented Locations**

⬜   **Distribution**

GRAY TREEFROG
Hyla versicolor

Physical Characteristics:

Gray treefrogs are 1 to 2 inches (3 to 5 cm) from snout to vent. The skin is a cryptic gray to green and changes with environmental conditions and activities, much like that of the Cope's gray treefrog. Warmer temperatures or green vegetation result in greener skin. Individuals are usually slightly larger and grayer than Cope's gray treefrogs. Gray treefrogs also have tough, warty skin in comparison to Cope's gray treefrogs. The back is covered with dark, black-bordered blotches. Blotches are more noticeable against the gray backs, but they are also visible against the green-colored backs. The belly appears white, inner thighs are yellow, and toes have small, adhesive pads similar to those of the Cope's gray treefrog. Also in common with the Cope's gray treefrog, gray treefrogs have a light spot beneath each eye. Males have dark throats during the breeding season. Males are smaller than females.

Taxonomy/Distribution and Status:

No subspecies is identified in South Dakota. Gray treefrogs range throughout the eastern United States. They are found in northeastern and southeastern South Dakota. Due to its rarity in South Dakota, the SDNHP monitors this species.

Habitat and Habits:

Gray treefrogs inhabit woodland habitats near wetlands, such as floodplain forests. In South Dakota, gray treefrogs frequently occur in highly vegetated semipermanent wetlands. They are often found in tall trees or shrubs, remaining in the shade during the day.

Gray treefrogs chorus from tall perches in trees or bushes. Calling perches are usually higher (>9 feet [3 m]) than those of Cope's gray treefrogs. Their melodic chorus of slow, low-pitched trills has a trill rate of 17 to 35 pulses per second, slower than that of the Cope's gray treefrog. Trill rate may be affected by temperature, similar to the Cope's gray treefrog. Calls are easy to hear due to their volume and the height of the calling perch.

The breeding season coincides with the breeding season of Cope's gray treefrogs, which starts in late May and ends in mid-June. Breeding areas include fishless temporary to permanent pools surrounded by vegetation, although gray treefrogs are considered a forest-associated species. During breeding, the male mounts the female in a position called amplexus and fertilizes her eggs as they are released. She lays up to 2,000 eggs in small clusters. Eggs hatch in four to five days as tadpoles, which grow into froglets in two months. Young frogs remain in short, thick vegetation until hibernation.

To survive the winter, gray treefrogs settle beneath leaf litter, logs, or rocks but above the frost line. Production of plasma glycerol in the liver and its circu-

Gray Treefrog   Carol Hall, Minnesota DNR

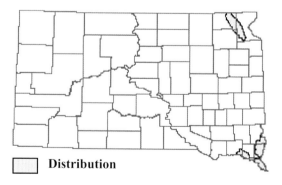

Distribution

lation to other organs protects the frog's cells from freeze damage. Gray treefrogs use both glycerol and glucose as antifreeze.

Gray treefrogs forage high in trees. They are more arboreal and better adapted to tree climbing than most frogs, with the exception of Cope's gray treefrog. As a result, gray treefrogs prey on both flying insects and terrestrial insects, such as beetles and caterpillars.

Remarks:

Gray treefrogs are similar to Cope's gray treefrogs in many ways. Their breeding calls help distinguish between them. However, temperature may affect the speed of the call trill rate; cool weather slows the trill rate speed.

Gray treefrogs and Cope's gray treefrogs are the only true treefrogs in South Dakota. Their toe pads allow them to vertically scale a tree or shrub, acting like suction cups to hold them tightly onto a tree or shrub.

Special References:

Layne, J. R., Jr., and A. L. Jones. 2001. Freeze tolerance in the gray treefrog: Cryoprotectant mobilization and organ dehydration. Journal of Experimental Zoology 290:1-5.

BOREAL CHORUS FROG
Pseudacris maculata

Physical Characteristics:

These small, slender-bodied frogs are 1 to 2 inches (2 to 4 cm) from snout to vent. The smooth-skinned body is gray to light brown. Boreal chorus frogs have five dark brown stripes down the back. Two of the stripes stretch from the nose through the eyes and to the groin. The central stripe typically forks at the rear. Stripes may be broken, giving the frog a spotted appearance. The belly is creamy white, and they may have marks on the throat and chest. This frog has a light-colored line along the upper lip, slightly enlarged toe pads, and indistinct webbing between the toes. They do not climb, as do other members of this family. A small, dark triangular spot may occur between the eyes. Males are generally smaller than females, and males develop dark brown or gray throats during the breeding season.

Taxonomy/Distribution and Status:

The boreal and western chorus frogs were previously considered subspecies of the species *Pseudacris triseriata*. Differences in morphology and calling between boreal chorus frogs (*P. t. maculata*) and western chorus frogs (*P. t. triseriata*) resulted in a classification change to *P. triseriata* for the western chorus frog and to *P. maculata* for the boreal chorus frog (Platz 1989). No subspecies is identified in South Dakota. The boreal chorus frog is the northernmost-ranging of the chorus frogs, found throughout the north central, central, and east central United States. They are common throughout South Dakota.

Habitat and Habits:

Boreal chorus frogs are primarily terrestrial frogs that occur in many habitats. They use grasslands near temporary to permanent wetlands with or without fish and agricultural or suburban areas, and they can adapt to dry conditions. They occupy wetlands during the breeding season and rest under stones or logs in low, damp areas near water.

Boreal chorus frogs are among the first frogs to emerge in the spring, usually in late March to early April. They breed from early April to late May or later in the Black Hills. They chorus to some extent during the day, but the most intense chorusing activity happens at night. Individuals occasionally call after the typical breeding season, apparently responding to cool, wet conditions.

Boreal chorus frogs usually call during the spring and summer from roadside ditches and nearly any wetland near grasslands. These frogs are most visible during the calling season. Their "preep, preep" calls last one to two seconds and resemble the trill of an insect. As air temperature warms, trill rates increase.

Females deposit up to 1,500 eggs in small masses of 5 to 300 eggs per mass. Eggs are deposited in shallow water of temporary wetlands, where the timing of hatching depends on the water temperature. The small (1 inch [3 cm]) tad-

Boreal Chorus Frog   Dan Fogell

Ventral surface   Aaron Gregor

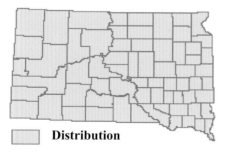

Distribution

41

pole has a clear dorsal fin. Tadpoles transform into froglets approximately two months later.

Boreal chorus frogs overwinter under rocks or logs or in animal burrows. In response to freezing, they release glucose via the bloodstream from glycogen stored in the liver. Glucose accumulates in cells, making boreal chorus frogs freeze-tolerant during cold weather. Ice crystals usually form outside the cells, where tissue damage is minimal. This characteristic allows species like boreal chorus frogs to survive cold weather.

Boreal chorus frogs eat small insects and spiders.

Remarks:

"Preep, preep" (roll r's) calls produced by chorus frogs are similar to running one's thumb across the teeth of a comb, saving the shortest teeth for last.

Special References:

Edwards, J. R., K. L. Koster, and D. L. Swanson. 2000. Time course for cryoprotectant synthesis in the freeze-tolerant chorus frog, *Pseudacris triseriata*. Comparative Biochemistry and Physiology Part A 125:367-375.

Platz, J. E. 1989. Speciation within the chorus frog (*Pseudacris triseriata*): Morphometric and mating call analyses of the boreal and western subspecies. Copeia 1989:704-712.

Swanson, D. L., B. M. Graves, and K. L. Koster. 1996. Freezing tolerance/ intolerance and cryoprotectant synthesis in terrestrially overwintering anurans in the Great Plains, USA. Journal of Comparative Physiology, B:Biochemical, Systematic, and Environmental Physiology 166:110-119.

Family Scaphiopodidae

The family Scaphiopodidae includes the spadefoot toads, which are adapted to arid habitats in North America. They have dark sharp-edged tubercles, called spades, on each hind foot that are used to dig burrows for hibernation and shelter. Spadefoots have short snouts, vertically elliptical pupils, relatively smooth skin, and teeth in the upper jaw. They lack parotid glands. Egg to toad transformation is accelerated, taking only two weeks. This adaptation to arid environments allows them to take advantage of short-lived temporary ponds.

PLAINS SPADEFOOT
Spea bombifrons

Physical Characteristics:

Plains spadefoots have stout bodies that measure 2 to 3 inches (4 to 5 cm) from snout to vent. The greenish-gray to brown skin is slightly textured with orange tubercles and speckled with dark brown or gray markings. Two to four indistinct stripes stretch along the back. The belly is white. Plains spadefoots have vertical pupils, much like cats. They also have large bosses between the eyes, and sharp, black, wedge-shaped spades on the hind feet. Males have bluish-gray throats and swollen forelegs, and they are usually smaller than females.

Taxonomy/Distribution and Status:

No subspecies is identified in South Dakota. Within the United States, plains spadefoots are primarily found in the Great Plains. They occur locally in western and southeastern South Dakota, but are apparently absent from the northeastern part of the state. This toad remains underground for extended periods and is often detected only after heavy rains, making it likely that it is more common than surveys and records indicate.

Habitat and Habits:

Plains spadefoots are common across the Great Plains, where they prefer grasslands or floodplains with sandy or loose soils and temporary wetlands.

Plains spadefoots rest in burrows during the day and surface to feed during the night, being most active after extensive rains. They are known as explosive breeders. They congregate to breed in large numbers in temporary wetlands after heavy late spring or summer rains. The call is a blaring, raspy "garvank" sound repeated in one half to one second intervals.

Females deposit up to 2,000 eggs in small masses of 10 to 250 eggs per mass. Eggs hatch in two days, with hatching time dependent on air temperature and oxygen content of the water. Tadpoles reach full size in 25 days. They may become cannibalistic when food is limited. Development from tadpole to frog occurs rapidly.

During nonbreeding periods, plains spadefoots use their foot spades to dig overwintering burrows in moist soils to depths greater than three feet.

43

Plains Spadefoot   Jeffrey B. LeClere

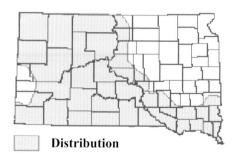

Distribution

Plains spadefoots feed at night on insect prey, such as beetles, crickets, and ants.

Remarks:

Most skin secretions produced by frogs and toads are poisonous. Plains spadefoots produce skin secretions that can cause severe allergic reactions or trigger asthma attacks in some people.

Special References:

Swanson, D. L., and B. M. Graves. 1995. Supercooling and freeze intolerance in overwintering juvenile spadefoot toads (*Scaphiopus bombifrons*). Journal of Herpetology 29:280-285.

Family Ranidae
The family Ranidae includes true frogs. North America has only one genus, *Lithobates*, in this family. True frogs have large breastbones, eyes with horizontal pupils, slender waists, long legs, pointed toes, and extensive webbing on the hind feet. They have smooth skin and dorsolateral folds along the center of the back, except for the bullfrog, which lacks dorsolateral folds.

PLAINS LEOPARD FROG
Lithobates blairi

Physical Characteristics:
The plains leopard frog measures 2 to 4 inches (5 to 10 cm) from snout to vent. This species can be distinguished from the northern leopard frog by its stocky body and short head. The plains leopard frog also has a small, distinct, light spot on each eardrum (tympanum), which is absent from the northern leopard frog's eardrum. The plains leopard frog usually has a dark spot on the snout and an obvious light line along the upper jaw. Plains leopard frogs have tan to gray skin with brown, circular marks, which may be bordered with pale coloration. The belly is white, and the groin is yellow. Two stripes run down the back on the dorsolateral folds, which may break up near the lower back. This last characteristic also helps distinguish the northern and plains leopard frogs.

Taxonomy/Distribution and Status:
Plains leopard frogs were recently reclassified from the genus *Rana* to *Lithobates* based on an analysis of evolutionary relationships among amphibians. No subspecies is identified in South Dakota. Plains leopard frogs range throughout the central United States, particularly in the central and southern Great Plains. Isolated populations also occur in Arizona and parts of the Midwest. This species is found in southeastern South Dakota. The plains leopard frog has also been reported from as far west as Badlands National Park. Additional surveys are needed to verify its state distribution. The SDNHP monitors this species because of its rarity in the state.

Habitat and Habits:
Plains leopard frogs use grasslands associated with permanent ponds or streams as their primary habitat. Because of habitat loss or degradation, they use a diversity of habitats such as roadside ditches and farm ponds. Plains leopard frogs are more drought tolerant than northern leopard frogs. Rarely do plains and northern leopard frogs coexist due to competition for available resources.

Individuals breed from late March to early June, usually beginning with the onset of warm rains. Males assemble in ponds and begin calling after sunset. The call consists of two to three separate blares per second, which sound like "chuck-chuck" or "chuck-chuck-chuck," similar to that of the northern leopard frog. It can be difficult to distinguish between plains and northern leopard frog

Plains Leopard Frog   Dan Fogell

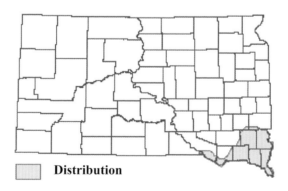

Distribution

calls without experience.

The male mounts the female. Her eggs are fertilized, then released in shallow water. A translucent, protective gel surrounds the round mass of up to 6,500 eggs. Eggs hatch as tadpoles in two to three weeks. Tadpoles grow into froglets approximately two months later. Plains leopard frogs burrow into the muddy bottom of ponds or streams with the onset of cold weather.

They feed primarily on terrestrial insects and spiders.

Remarks:

All leopard frogs were considered the same species until the 1970s, when genetic differences were detected. The leopard frog species group was then separated into four species: southern leopard frog (*Rana sphenocephala*), plains leopard frog, northern leopard frog (*R. pipiens*), and Rio Grande leopard frog (*R. berlandieri*).

Special References:

Ernst, J. A. 2001. Assessment of the *Rana pipiens* complex in southwestern South Dakota. M.S. Thesis. University of Wisconsin, Stevens Point, Wisconsin. 50pp.

BULLFROG
Lithobates catesbeiana

Physical Characteristics:
The bullfrog is the largest South Dakotan anuran, measuring 4 to 6 inches (9 and 15 cm) from snout to vent. Skin color and shade depend on the individual's size and on air temperature. Small frogs are usually paler, and warm weather results in paler frogs. The head is slightly paler than the body. The white or yellow belly has sporadic gray mottling. Bullfrogs lack ridges along the back, although they have small, circular ridges around the eardrums. Hind legs are spotted or banded, and the hind feet are completely webbed, except for the last joint of the longest toe. Males are usually darker than females, with occasional green and brown mottling across the back. Males also have large, convex eardrums, whereas females have small, flat eardrums. Males develop yellow throats during the breeding season.

Taxonomy/Distribution and Status:
Bullfrogs were reclassified from the genus *Rana* to *Lithobates* based on genetic data. No subspecies is identified in South Dakota. The bullfrog ranges throughout the eastern United States, extending into the plains states south of South Dakota. Bullfrogs have been widely introduced, and populations are now found in many locations where they were not native.

This species was historically found in a few south central and southeastern South Dakota counties. Introductions make it difficult to determine the natural distribution pattern.

Introductions of bullfrogs are causes for concern, since bullfrogs can extirpate other frog species. Recent surveys indicate that northern cricket frogs are no longer present in the Keya Paha River in South Dakota, where bullfrogs are abundant, suggesting that bullfrogs may have displaced other native frog populations.

Habitat and Habits:
Males establish and maintain strong territories during the breeding season. These highly aquatic frogs usually select large water bodies with emergent vegetation and open water. In South Dakota, bullfrogs are associated with large permanent and semipermanent wetlands and river floodplains.

Bullfrogs breed relatively late in the year, usually from June to mid-July, when males begin calling from their territories. They are among the latest breeders of South Dakota frogs. Calls are a series of loud baritone notes that sound like "jug-a-rum." Males often call on warm summer nights from midnight to sunrise.

Females lay up to 20,000 eggs in large masses on the surface of the water. Eggs hatch in four to five days. Tadpoles are green to brown with small spots on the back, sides, and tail. Because of their long growth period, conversion from tadpole to adult takes an additional two to three years. As a result, tadpoles require permanent, deep waters.

Bullfrog

Dan Fogell

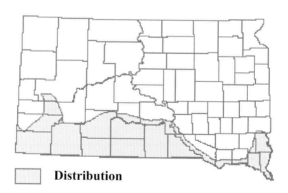

Distribution

Bullfrogs have the longest growth period among frogs found in South Dakota. Development continues after adulthood; bullfrogs reach sexual maturity in two to five years. Individuals burrow into the mud of deep ponds to hibernate.

Bullfrogs are opportunistic predators, preying on any animal they can catch and swallow. When introduced into wetlands, bullfrogs can reduce or eliminate other amphibians. Adults eat small mammals, snakes, and invertebrates. Tadpoles eat algae.

Remarks:

Fried frog legs from bullfrogs is a common dish in southern states.

NORTHERN LEOPARD FROG
Lithobates pipiens

Physical Characteristics:

Northern leopard frogs measure 2 to 4 inches from snout to vent (5 to 9 cm). The brown to green skin has large, circular, black spots found irregularly across the back. They also have continuous, cream-colored dorsolateral folds extending across the back to the groin, unlike the plains leopard frog, which has discontinuous folds. The rust-colored eardrums lack a distinct, central light mark, a characteristic that helps distinguish the northern from the plains leopard frog. The northern leopard frog has a white belly, yellow legs on the underside, and banded or spotted hind legs.

In addition to the normal and common color morph, this species has two additional and rarer color morphs - Burnsi and Kandiyohi. Burnsi frogs have black spots only along the legs. Kandiyohi frogs have additional black markings between their black spots when compared to the normal color morph.

Males have visible vocal sacs and large, round thumbs during the breeding season.

Taxonomy/Distribution and Status:

Northern leopard frogs were reclassified to the genus *Lithobates* from *Rana* due to an extensive phylogenetic study on amphibians. No subspecies is identified in South Dakota. This species has a broad geographical distribution, ranging in the northern United States and Canada, although western populations are declining. The northern leopard frog is found throughout South Dakota and seems to be stable in the state.

Habitat and Habits:

Northern leopard frogs occur in and around semipermanent and permanent wetlands statewide. They begin calling in mid-April and continue to late May, depending on elevation. The calls are long, deep snores and short grunts that sound like a motorboat. Some calls have one, two, or more syllables, which may last up to three seconds with a pulse rate of 20 calls per second. Calls are cryptic and infrequent, and this species may go unnoticed during the calling season.

Females deposit eggs on submerged vegetation in shallow water, releasing up to 6,000 eggs in several gelatinous masses. Eggs hatch in 10 to 15 days. Tadpoles transform into froglets in approximately three months. With the onset of cold weather, northern leopard frogs retreat to the muddy bottoms of permanent water bodies, such as lakes and rivers.

Northern leopard frogs feed on insects and spiders.

Remarks:

Northern leopard frogs are also known as meadow or grass frogs due to their presence in backyards, pastures, or meadows during the summer.

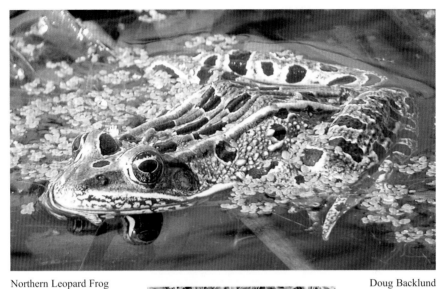

Northern Leopard Frog   Doug Backlund

Burnsi color morph   Mick Zerr

Kandiyohi color morph   Jodi L. Massie and Ben G. Blake

They are often used as laboratory animals for dissection and educational purposes, especially in high schools.

Special References:

Hardy, D. G. 1972. Some population dynamics of *Rana pipiens* in an area of southeastern South Dakota. M.A. Thesis. University of South Dakota, Vermillion, South Dakota. 49pp.

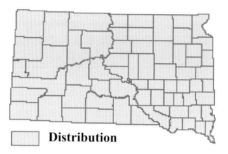

☐ **Distribution**

WOOD FROG
Lithobates sylvaticus

Physical Characteristics:

Wood frogs measure 1 to 3 inches (4 to 7 cm) from snout to vent. The skin is brown with a reddish hue. Wood frogs lack prominent markings on the back, although they may have a pale middorsal stripe. They also have two dorsolateral folds across the back, which may have dark dashed lines on top of them. The belly is sometimes dusted with markings. Wood frogs also have a dark mask that surrounds the eyes and extends to the back of the eardrums. The upper jaw has a pale band. Males are usually darker and smaller than females. Males may also develop enlarged thumbs and evident vocal sacs above the foreleg during the breeding season.

Taxonomy/Distribution and Status:

Wood frogs were reclassified to the genus *Lithobates* from *Rana* because of findings from an extensive phylogenetic study on amphibians. No subspecies is identified in South Dakota. Wood frogs range as far north as the Arctic Circle, giving them the northernmost distribution of any member of the Ranidae family. A well-developed capacity for tolerating freezing allows this northern distribution. Wood frogs occur in the northeastern and extreme north central United States.

There are two wood frog records from the 1920s in northeastern South Dakota, but whether a population still existed in the state remained a mystery until wood frogs were detected in Roberts County during anuran calling surveys in 1997-1998 (Fischer 1998). Jessen and Skadsen have since surveyed other sites in northeastern South Dakota and rediscovered additional populations in prairie potholes and creeks in this region (Backlund 2005). The known current state distribution is extreme northeastern South Dakota. Due to its rarity in South Dakota, the SDNHP monitors this species.

Habitat and Habits:

Wood frogs inhabit cool, moist woodlands, such as mixed woodlands, coulees, and floodplain forests. South Dakota habitats include coulees and semi-permanent and permanent wetlands interspersed with flooded trees. Wood frogs wander a substantial distance from water, usually after they breed. They have a secretive and solitary lifestyle.

Wood frogs are early, explosive breeders. Breeding begins in late March or early April following snowmelt and continues for less than one month. Frogs call and breed in small, fishless, temporary ponds or coulees near meadows or woodlands. Their "waaaduck" calls sound similar to ducks quacking and are repeated two to three times per second.

After attracting a female, the male mounts her in a position called amplexus. He fertilizes the eggs as she releases them. She releases up to 1,000

Wood Frog

Carol Hall, Minnesota DNR

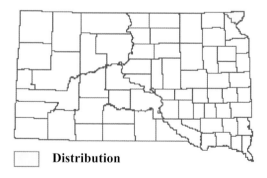

Distribution

eggs in a small, condensed circular ball in a communal nesting location in shallow water. Eggs hatch in two to three weeks as olive brown tadpoles. The wood frog's rapid tadpole development period lasts up to two months.

Wood frogs overwinter under leaf litter, rocks, or logs or in small mammal burrows. These frogs actually freeze, but cells are protected from damage because of the accumulation of glucose.

Diet includes invertebrates, such as flies, grasshoppers, beetles, and crickets.

Remarks:

Wood frogs are adapted to breed in pools filled by spring rains and snowmelt, exposing them to a variety of acidic conditions. As a result, they can breed and survive in low pH environments. Despite this tolerance, low pH levels may affect egg survival and larval development, resulting in possible deformities.

Special References:

Storey, K. B. 1987. Glycolysis and the regulation of cryoprotectant synthesis in liver of the freeze tolerant wood frog. Journal of Comparative Physiology B157:373-380.

REPTILES

About 8,000 reptile species are known worldwide, with approximately 216 reptile species found in North America. South Dakota has two orders, eight families, 23 genera, and 31 species.

The outer layer of reptilian skin is composed of scales in the case of lizards and snakes or external plates in turtles. Reptiles can tolerate more arid habitats than can amphibians, since their skin prevents water loss and provides protection. This makes reptiles generally less dependent on water than amphibians. Some reptiles require little water from their environment, but some are fully aquatic, leaving water only to lay eggs. Old skin is shed as reptiles grow. Young reptiles grow more rapidly and shed more often than adults.

Fertilization of eggs occurs internally in reptiles. Some species are oviparous. Females may store sperm in reproductive tracts and fertilize eggs several months after breeding. Young usually develop in a hard-shelled egg. The relatively hard shells of reptile eggs facilitate egg laying in terrestrial habitats. Few reptiles guard eggs or protect nests.

Other reptile species are ovoviviparous. In this case, young snakes and lizards develop inside the female in a thin, transparent membrane and are born alive. Live birth is a more advanced method of reproduction, since it may help deter losses to nest predation.

Reptiles lack a larval stage like amphibians. Instead, young are typically small replicas of their parents when they hatch or are born.

Reptiles breathe using lungs. Some more aquatic species can hold their breath for long periods. Special membranes in the throat and cloaca of some aquatic species allow small amounts of dissolved oxygen to be absorbed to meet oxygen requirements. These more aquatic reptiles can stay underwater for long periods of time.

Reptiles rarely vocalize, and they hear poorly. Snakes are assumed to be deaf or nearly so, although they are thought to sense low frequency vibrations through their skin. Reptiles have a well-developed sense of smell. A snake uses its tongue to smell by sending samples of air and particles to the Jacobson's organ, a chemosensory organ located behind the nostrils in the roof of the mouth. This organ consists of pits covered with chemically-sensitive nerve endings to provide sensory feedback for detecting airborne chemicals. Reptiles also have relatively good vision. Snakes often detect movement with their eyes, and visual cues help them locate prey or attract mates.

A turtle shell is made of an upper shell, called the carapace, and a lower shell, called the plastron. The shell is formed from bony plates fused with parts of the spinal column and ribs and covered by keratinous scales, called scutes. Old keratin layers are shed as a new layer of keratin grows beneath. Shells may be hard or soft. Turtles have claws and lack teeth. Males often have concave plastrons and longer tails with vents that extend farther beyond the shell's edge, when compared to females. Turtles may be herbivores, carnivores, or omnivores.

Lizards are closely related to snakes. Most lizards have four limbs with claws on their toes. Unlike snakes, lizards have ear openings, and their eyelids open and close. Eyes are typically on the sides of the head. Lizards have long, slender bodies, an outer covering of scales, and long tails. Scales are shed in patches as the lizard grows. In some species, the tail can grow back if it is broken off. Males have tails with enlarged bases, particularly during the breeding season, since this is where the hemipenes, the male reproductive organs, are stored. Lizards can be carnivores, herbivores, or omnivores, although those found in South Dakota are carnivorous.

Snakes lack ear openings and limbs, though they are sensitive to vibrations. Instead of eyelids, snakes have hard spectacles, which are scales covering the eyes. Scales covering the bodies and tail are shed as the animal grows. Snakes shed by crawling out of their skin, and in the process, their skin is turned inside out. Males often have a longer tail and a broader tail base than the female. During copulation, the male snake may have an enlarged tail base due to the hemipenes. He may bite the female on the neck or head during copulation. All snakes are carnivorous and capture prey by three different methods; seizing and swallowing without constriction (gartersnakes and others), suffocation through constriction (gophersnakes), and poisoning by venom (rattlesnakes). Snakes can swallow prey whole due to their flexible jaws. Bone articulation, joints, and ligaments in the skull help the jaws flex and expand, allowing snakes to eat prey larger than their heads.

Reptiles are unique animals with different life cycles and physical characteristics than amphibians. Because of their ability to internally fertilize eggs and produce hard-shelled amniotic eggs, reptiles can exploit many habitats. Turtles, snakes, and lizards each have their own distinguishing features. Like amphibians, reptiles play an important role in nature as part of the food chain.

Order Testudines

The order Testudines includes turtles and tortoises. No tortoises occur in South Dakota. Turtles and tortoises are found on all continents except Antarctica. Turtle and tortoise shells are made of 59 to 61 fused vertebrae and may reach lengths of 4 to 73 inches (10 to 185 cm).

Family Chelydridae

The family Chelydridae includes snapping turtles, which inhabit freshwater habitats. The family includes two genera, one of which occurs in South Dakota.

SNAPPING TURTLE
Chelydra serpentina

Description:

Snapping turtles are heavy-bodied turtles. Adults measure 7 to 17 inches (17 to 44 cm) in carapace length and weigh an average of 12.8 pounds (5,800 g). This is South Dakota's largest turtle. The largest snapping turtle documented in South Dakota was a female that weighed 44 pounds.

Snapping turtles are easy to distinguish from other South Dakota turtles because of the long tail, large head, reduced plastron, and rough carapace. The tail has noticeable saw-toothed scales, the "X" shaped plastron is yellow, and the carapace is tan/brown with three rows of small keels. The keels are more prominent in young turtles and are often covered by algae and mud. Snapping turtles also have serrations bordering the back edge of the shell. Snapping turtles have black streaks speckled across the head and large tubercles covering the neck. Their large, flat feet have long claws. Females are slightly larger than males, and the female's cloacal opening is closer to the carapace than is the male's.

Taxonomy/Distribution and Status:

The subspecies found in South Dakota is the common snapping turtle (*C. s. serpentina*). Snapping turtles range throughout the eastern United States east of the Rocky Mountains. They range statewide in South Dakota wherever permanent water is available, where they can be quite common. The snapping turtle is one of the two most common turtles in the state.

Habitat and Habits:

Snapping turtles are highly aquatic and restricted to permanent water with soft mud bottoms and adequate vegetation. During the day, they bury themselves in the mud of shallow wetlands or float near the water's surface. They stretch their head above the water, exposing their nostrils to breathe. Snapping turtles are rarely observed basking in the sun because they cannot tolerate high temperatures, but they may travel overland between ponds. They can become agitated and aggressive if encountered by people.

Snapping Turtle   Lauren J. Livo and Steve Wilcox

Carapace   Melissa Hough

Plastron   Josh Kiesow

Snapping turtles breed from April to October. The male and female court by facing each other, moving their heads and necks from side to side (opposite each other), and swallowing water, then forcing it out their nostrils. The pair mates in warm water. The male mounts the female, wrapping his tail around her shell to align their cloacal openings. She then remains passive while he penetrates and releases his sperm. The female may retain the potent sperm for several years. Females deposit up to 90 round, white, rubbery eggs in terrestrial nests, usually in June. Snapping turtles may lay one or two clutches of eggs per year.

Nests are 4 to 7 inches (10 to 18 cm) deep and located in sandy areas near water. Eggs hatch in two to five months. Sex of the young turtles is determined by incubation temperature; higher temperatures produce females, and lower temperatures result in males. Snapping turtles are sexually mature at five to seven years of age. They overwinter in the mud bottom of ponds.

Snapping turtles forage on a variety of prey, ranging from aquatic plants to mollusks, fish, and birds. Snapping turtles in southeastern South Dakota mainly eat fish and terrestrial vertebrates, using their mouth and feet to tear the meat or vegetation apart while underwater.

Remarks:

Snapping turtles are pursued as game and for meat. Use caution when handling them. They are aggressive and powerful and have a long neck and strong jaws. It is best to carry them by the hind limbs with the plastron directed towards one's legs. Handling large snapping turtles by the base of the tail may cause severe damage to the turtle's spinal cord.

Special References:

Darrow, T. D. 1961. Food habits of western painted and snapping turtles in southeastern South Dakota and eastern Nebraska. M.A. Thesis. University of South Dakota, Vermillion, South Dakota. 37pp.

Hammer, D. A. 1968. Snapping turtle life history on Lacreek Refuge, South Dakota. M.S. Thesis, South Dakota State University, Brookings, South Dakota. 56pp.

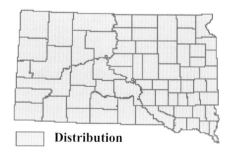

Distribution

Family Emydidae

The family Emydidae includes semiaquatic pond turtles, which are mainly fresh-water genera. Members of this order are usually omnivorous and have solid plastrons, although there are a few exceptions.

PAINTED TURTLE
Chrysemys picta

Description:

Painted turtles have smooth, unkeeled carapaces that measure 3 to 9 inches (9 to 23 cm) in length in adults. The average weight is 1 pound (450 g).

These attractive turtles have olive or brown carapaces decorated with a network of darker lines. The red-orange plastrons have black and yellow streaks, and the plastron colors are brighter in juveniles than in adults. Painted turtles have an intricate shell pattern with minimal red margins and indistinct yellow stripes on the carapace. The shell lacks serrations on the rear edge of the shell. The head, legs, and neck are black or olive, and the neck and legs are streaked with yellow stripes. Painted turtles have a small notch on the front, upper jaw. Males have longer claws, thicker tails, and smaller carapaces than females. The male's cloacal opening is farther from the edge of the shell than that of the female.

Taxonomy/Distribution and Status:

The subspecies recognized in South Dakota is the western painted turtle (*C. p. bellii*), which is the largest subspecies in size. Painted turtles are found across the eastern United States. Scattered populations exist in western states, including Arizona, Colorado, Texas, New Mexico, and Utah. This is the most common turtle in South Dakota, and it is found in almost every permanent body of water throughout the state.

Habitat and Habits:

Painted turtles live in and around ponds with shoreline vegetation; soft, muddy bottoms; and partially submerged rocks or logs for basking. They are found wherever permanent water conditions occur, but they may also occupy temporary wetlands in South Dakota.

Painted turtles are active during the day, resting on logs or rocks in a pond, where they are easily observed. Individuals may bask for up to two hours several times during the day, alternating with foraging periods. Painted turtles share basking sites with other turtles of the same or different species.

Courtship and breeding take place from May to early June. Courtship involves a repetitive chase-and-follow effort with eventual contact between a male and female. The male ultimately faces the female and strokes her face and neck with his claws. She eventually responds by touching him on the underside of his forearms, after which he responds by selecting an area to mate. The female follows, and they sink to the bottom of the wetland to breed.

Painted Turtles

Doug Backlund

Plastron

Andrew Kopp

64

The male mounts the female, curls his tail under her shell, aligns their cloacal openings, and copulates. A female lays more than 20 elongate, leathery-shelled eggs during June. Eggs are laid in sandy areas in a nest that is on a slight south-facing slope and located approximately 5 inches (12 cm) below the surface of the sand. Eggs hatch in two to three months, usually in August. Sex determination is temperature dependent; high temperatures produce females, and low temperatures produce males. Painted turtles reach maturity in four to six years.

Adult turtles overwinter for five to six months in a soft-bottomed wetland usually at depths of less than 7 feet (two meters). Hatchling turtles overwinter in a shallow terrestrial natal nest that is typically 3 to 6 inches (8 to 14 cm) deep. The site may be subjected to temperatures as low as 14°F (–10°C). Hatchlings can tolerate a brief exposure to freezing with up to 50 percent of their body water becoming ice, as long as nest temperatures remain above 39°F (4°C). However, survival at lower temperatures requires the ability to supercool to avoid freezing. Hatchling turtles can survive prolonged periods of supercooling to 14°F (–10°C), which is accomplished by winter decreases in both the supercooling capacity and the resistance to penetration of external ice into the body from the surrounding soil.

Painted turtles are omnivores that eat aquatic vegetation, insects, and crayfish. They also scavenge for food.

Remarks:

Reticulate melanism occurs in northern populations of male western painted turtles (Bandas 2003). This is characterized by a black, netlike carapace pattern that overlies the normal carapace pattern.

Painted turtles are often caught, kept as pets, and then released in areas where they may be unable to survive. Painted turtles carry disease, such as salmonella, so there is some disease risk when keeping these turtles as pets. Releasing captive animals into the wild can introduce diseases into wild populations and should be avoided.

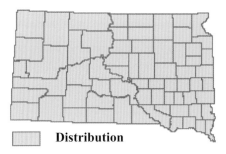

Distribution

Special References:

Bandas, S. J. 2003. Geographic distribution and morphometrics of South Dakota turtles. M.S. Thesis. South Dakota State University, Brookings, South Dakota. 106pp.

Churchill, T. A., and K. B. Storey. 1992. Natural freezing survival by painted turtles *Chrysemys picta marginata* and *C. p. bellii*. American Journal of Physiology 262:R530-R537.

Darrow, T. D. 1961. Food habits of western painted and snapping turtles in southeastern South Dakota and eastern Nebraska. M.A. Thesis. University of South Dakota, Vermillion, South Dakota. 37pp.

Gronke, W. K., S. R. Chipps, S. J. Bandas, and K. F. Higgins. 2006. Reticulate melanism in western painted turtles (*Chrysemys picta bellii*): Exploring linkages with habitat and heating rates. American Midland Naturalist 156:289-298.

Packard, G. C., and M. J. Packard. 2001. The overwintering strategy of hatchling painted turtles, or how to survive in the cold without freezing. BioScience 51:199-207.

Storey, K. B., J. M. Storey, S. P. J. Brooks, T. A. Churchill, and R. J. Brooks. 1988. Hatchling turtles survive freezing during winter hibernation. Proceedings of Natural Academy of Sciences USA 85:8350-8354.

BLANDING'S TURTLE
Emys blandingii

Description:
Blanding's turtles range from 5 to 7 inches (13 to 18 cm) in carapace length. The bluish-black carapace is smooth, oval, dome-shaped, and speckled with numerous yellow spots, which are more noticeable in juveniles. The yellow plastron is bordered with black blotches and hinged at the front third of the shell. This hinge raises the plastron, allowing Blanding's turtles to move their soft body parts under the hard, protective shell. This turtle has a bright yellow chin, throat, and neck, while the appendages and top and sides of the head are blue-gray. Other characteristics include a long neck, protruding eyes, and a notched upper jaw. Males differ from females by having a longer tail, slightly indented and concave plastron, and a protruding anal opening.

Taxonomy/Distribution and Status:
No subspecies is recognized in South Dakota. Blanding's turtles range from the Great Lakes region west to Iowa, South Dakota, Missouri, and Nebraska. Small populations occur in the eastern United States. There are a few records of Blanding's turtles in southeastern South Dakota, but no viable population has been documented. This species is considered the rarest turtle in South Dakota, and as a result, the SDNHP monitors the Blanding's turtle.

Habitat and Habits:
Blanding's turtles are active during the day and often bask on logs, banks, and clumps of vegetation. They favor wet prairies with wetland complexes and creeks with abundant aquatic vegetation, organic bottoms, and adjacent sandy uplands. This turtle is primarily aquatic, although they will travel long distances overland.

Individuals begin to court and breed in April and continue through May. Blanding's turtles have a long and unique courtship period that involves a series of steps lasting several hours. Courtship involves males chasing, mounting, biting, and stimulating females. When a male mounts a female, he exposes his yellow throat by swaying and extending his head in front of her. When the female becomes submissive, she extends her tail to accept the male. After copulation, she selects a nesting site in open, sparsely-vegetated soil.

Nesting lasts from May to June. The female digs a flask-shaped nest 7 inches (18 cm) deep. She deposits an average of 10 off-white, malleable eggs per clutch. Eggs hatch in two months, with temperature of the nest determining the sex of the embryos. Blanding's turtles reach sexual maturity in 14 to 20 years.

Individuals overwinter in organic substrates of shallow ponds, typically near their summer habitats. They also may estivate during warm temperatures.

Blanding's turtles eat plants and animals, including succulent vegetation, insects, crayfish, and fish.

Blanding's Turtle carapace   Dan Fogell

Plastron   Tom Jessen

⊙   **Documented Locations**

68

Remarks:

This turtle is also known as the "semibox" turtle because of its hinged plastron.

The common name is derived from William Blanding, an early naturalist from Philadelphia.

FALSE MAP TURTLE
Graptemys pseudogeographica

Description:

The carapace length in adults measures 9 to 10 inches (23 to 25 cm) in females and 4 to 6 inches (11 to 15 cm) in males. As young turtles reach maturity, the shell becomes more elongate. Weight averages 1.6 pounds (450 g). The carapace is brown to olive with round light markings and dark blotches on each shell section, or scute. The carapace also has indistinct yellow lines that form a netlike outline, prominent ridges (keels) that extend through the center of the back, and serrated edges extending along the rear edge of the shell. The yellow plastron has dark lines surrounding its margins and seams, forming a pattern of light and dark stripes. The shell design fades and edge projections on the shell become dull as false map turtles age. Bright yellow lines mark the head, neck, and appendages. A characteristic yellow "L" is mirrored across the top of their head.

Females are approximately 1.5 times larger than males. Males also have longer, thicker tails and longer foreclaws than females.

Taxonomy/Distribution and Status:

The subspecies recognized in South Dakota is the false map turtle (*G. p. pseudogeographica*), the largest subspecies in size. This species is found in the lower Missouri River and throughout the Mississippi River. False map turtles are most common in the Missouri River in southeastern South Dakota. They can be found locally northward in the Missouri River to the North Dakota border. State law currently protects this species as a state threatened species. Due to its rarity in South Dakota, the SDNHP monitors this species.

Habitat and Habits:

False map turtles use large rivers, backwater habitats, lakes, or flooded floodplains. In South Dakota, false map turtles seem to avoid reservoirs and appear to reside most commonly in backwater habitats of the Missouri River. Within their selected habitats, they require many basking sites and some aquatic vegetation. Individuals are active during the day and usually observed basking on partially submerged rocks or logs.

False map turtles court in wetlands in the spring. A male swims around a female, eventually stopping to face her. He then begins to drum the female on her head with his foreclaws. He bobs his head up and down while touching her. This stimulates her to mate, causing her to sink down to the substrate and signaling him to mount her. Copulation occurs when their cloacal openings align.

The female digs a flask-shaped nest 4 to 6 inches (10 to 16 cm) deep in a sandy area near water and with minimal vegetation (but sometimes with low shrubs). She begins laying eggs in June and continues through July, laying 12 to 16 white, elliptical, rubbery eggs.

False Map Turtles   NEBRASKAland Magazine/Nebraska Game and Parks Commission

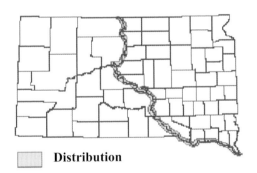

Distribution

Eggs hatch approximately two months later, in August or September. As with other turtles, incubation temperature determines the sex of the young. A female may produce up to three clutches during one reproductive season. False map turtles overwinter in the mud or in muskrat dens in wetlands. Dry winters may harm these turtles due to the potential of encountering subfreezing temperatures, which increase winterkills.

False map turtles typically feed in the early morning on insects, crayfish, dead fish, and aquatic plants. Young turtles are primarily carnivorous, whereas adults are mainly herbivorous.

Remarks:

South Dakota state law protects this species from harvest.

WESTERN BOX TURTLE
Terrapene ornata

Description:

The adult's carapace is 4 to 5 inches (10 to 13 cm) in length. The dark brown carapace is flat-topped, unkeeled, and distinguished by yellow lines and spots. These yellow lines radiate outward and downward from three points on either side of the carapace. Each shell section, or scute, typically has five to nine yellow streaks. The carapace is also strongly curved and arched. The light brown plastron has yellow streaks and mottling and is usually similar in length to the carapace. There is individual variation in the color pattern. Western box turtles have yellow spots speckled over the dark brown to greenish limbs and head and a yellow stripe on the top of the short tail. A faint line runs down the middle of the carapace.

A male can turn its first hind toe inward at a sharp angle to embrace a female while they are breeding. Males have red eyes, whereas females have green or yellowish brown eyes. As in other turtle species, females are larger than males.

Taxonomy/Distribution and Status:

The subspecies found in South Dakota is the ornate box turtle (*T. o. ornata*). Western box turtles range throughout the central United States as far north as South Dakota and as far south as Texas and New Mexico. The distribution is discontinuous in the northeastern portion of the range. The species is found primarily in sandy areas of south central South Dakota. Due to its rarity in South Dakota, the SDNHP monitors this species.

Habitat and Habits:

Western box turtle habitats include open grasslands/pastures, open fields, open woodlands, and dry, sandy areas. They are highly terrestrial and do not depend on the presence of water, allowing them to tolerate arid conditions.

Western box turtles are active during the day, when they are often found basking, feeding, or resting. Daily activity begins just after sunrise and ends just before sunset. They use shallow "forms," or burrows as night retreats. Western box turtles are most active following periods of warm, rainy weather, which initiates their spring emergence after a long overwintering period.

Males nudge and push females to entice them to begin mating in the spring. The male hooks his claws at the end of the female's shell, and she wraps her limbs around him. Once their cloacal openings align, copulation takes place. They remain in this position for 30 minutes to two hours.

After copulation, she prepares for egg deposition by digging a shallow depression in loose soil or sand. She lays four to six eggs in the nest in late May or early June, nesting once each year. Eggs hatch in approximately two months. Turtles become sexually mature in seven to eight years. With the onset of cold weather in the fall, western box turtles dig underground burrows or use

Western Box Turtle carapace   Doug Backlund

Plastron   Doug Backlund

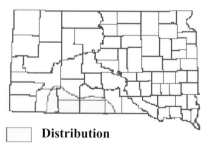

Distribution

74

existing burrows of other animals as overwintering sites in burrows as deep as 18 inches (46 cm).

This species was once mistakenly thought to be a predator on game bird nests. Food items include plants and insects, such as grasshoppers and dung beetles.

Remarks:

Western box turtles are often collected for the international pet trade. The Convention on International Trade in Endangered Species of Wild Fauna and Flora (CITES) currently regulates the trade of western box turtles to eliminate or minimize the illegal pet trade and protect this turtle.

When western box turtles are disturbed or attacked by animals, they retract the head, limbs, and tail into the shell and close the front of the plastron. Because of this ability, they are immune to injury by animals, except for those caused by humans. Road mortality is a cause of mortality for this species.

Special References:

Timken, R. L. 1969. Ornate box turtle distribution in South Dakota.
    Herpetologica 25:70.

Family Trionychidae

The family Trionychidae includes the softshell turtles. Their shells are soft, flat, and covered with leathery skin rather than keratinous scutes. Members of this family are found mainly in freshwater habitats.

SMOOTH SOFTSHELL
Apalone mutica

Description:

The adult's carapace length is 7 to 14 inches (17 to 36 cm) in females and 5 to 7 inches (12 to 18 cm) in males. They weigh an average of 2.8 pounds (1,270 g). They are named for their characteristically smooth, round, flat carapace, which is olive-gray to tan. The carapace has dark spots in juveniles and indistinct spots in adults. The plastron is white to yellow and hingeless, so they cannot retract their head, as can other turtles. The limbs are olive to orange above and white to gray below. A distinctive pale, black-bordered line stretches through the eye onto the neck. They also have faint lines across the muzzle and behind the eyes. These softshells do not have tubercles on the front of the carapace and do not have ridges in the nostrils. They also lack strong mottling or streaking on the webbed feet.

Adult females are typically 1.5 times larger than adult males. Males have relatively long tails with the cloacal opening near the tip of the tail, whereas females have relatively short tails with the cloacal opening beneath the carapace.

Taxonomy/Distribution and Status:

The subspecies recognized in South Dakota is the midland smooth softshell (*A. m. mutica*). Smooth softshells thrive in major river drainages of the central United States, particularly the Mississippi, Ohio, and Missouri rivers and major drainages within Alabama and Arkansas. In South Dakota, they frequent the free-flowing sections of the Missouri River. Some smooth softshells may also use reservoirs and other tributaries. For example, a smooth softshell was captured in the Cheyenne River, and sightings have been recorded from the Big Sioux River. Due to its rarity in South Dakota, the SDNHP monitors this species.

Habitat and Habits:

Smooth softshells are highly aquatic turtles, residing primarily in large rivers and streams with moderate to fast currents. They may also use lakes and impoundments. In South Dakota, smooth softshells mainly inhabit the free-flowing section of the Missouri River, with some use of large reservoirs. Rivers with sandy bottoms with few rocks and minimal aquatic vegetation are preferred habitat.

Individuals breed after hibernation, usually in April or May and may sometimes breed twice a year. Smooth softshells exhibit passive mating techniques. A male searches for a receptive female at basking sites. Unreceptive females res-

Smooth Softshell   Dan Fogell

Front view of nostrils

Plastron   Doug Backlund

pond by biting males, while a receptive female allows a male to mount her.

The female prepares for egg deposition by selecting a nest location in sparsely-vegetated, damp sandbars adjacent to water. She excavates a nest to a depth of up to 12 inches (30 cm). Nesting may occur from May through July, with nesting in South Dakota commonly occurring in June. The female deposits 14 eggs into the excavated nest. Eggs hatch two to three months later, in August or September. Smooth softshells have genetic sex determination rather than temperature-dependent sex determination, so sex ratios are relatively equal.

Males reach sexual maturity in four years, whereas females are sexually mature at age seven. These turtles overwinter buried in the substrate beneath the water. A communal overwintering site found in the Missouri River in southeastern South Dakota had more than 100 smooth softshells resting on the substrate a few feet below the water's surface.

Smooth softshells search for food in the early morning and late evening. They feed primarily on insects, although fish, plant material, and other terrestrial or aquatic animals may supplement their diet.

Remarks:

The smooth softshell is also known as the "spineless softshell." These turtles are passive and nonterritorial, though they can fight with courage if needed. The name refers to the lack of small tubercles present on the carapace.

Smooth softshells survive underwater for long periods due to their ability to absorb oxygen from the water through membranes in the mouth and cloaca.

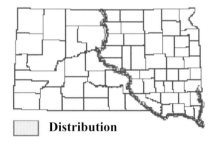

Distribution

SPINY SOFTSHELL
Apalone spinifera

Description:

Adult spiny softshells have an average carapace length of 4 to 15 inches (10 to 37 cm) in males and 8 to 16 inches (21 to 41 cm) in females. Adults weigh an average of 4.5 pounds (2,050 g). Their flat, round, leathery carapace becomes more elongated as they grow. The plastron is white to yellow and hingeless.

Spiny softshells vary in shell texture and coloration from smooth softshells. The olive-gray carapace is encircled by a black line and speckled with dark, circular spots (ocelli), especially near the center of the shell. Small, spiny projections near the front of the shell feel like sandpaper on males and appear as large bumps on females. Spiny softshells also differ from smooth softshells in other ways. The spiny softshell's webbed feet have strong streaking, and the tubular nose has noticeably ridged nostrils inside the nasal opening. Two streaks are present on the side of the head, one running from the corner of the jaw and another from each eye onto the neck.

Males have relatively long tails with the cloacal opening beyond the outside edge of the carapace. The female has a shorter tail, and the cloacal opening is beneath the carapace. Adult females generally lack ocelli but may have irregular mottling, while adult males and juveniles of both sexes have distinct ocelli. Females are larger than males.

Taxonomy/Distribution and Status:

The subspecies recognized in South Dakota is the western spiny softshell (*A. s. hartwegi*). Spiny softshells are found across much of the eastern United States, with disjunct populations found in the northeastern United States. The species is also found in the Colorado and Rio Grande rivers and several rivers in Montana. In semiarid to arid parts of their western range, rivers provide the only suitable habitat for spiny softshells, whereas in areas farther east, various wetland types provide suitable habitat.

Spiny softshells inhabit large tributaries of the Missouri River more commonly than the Missouri River itself. This species is less common in the Missouri River than the smooth softshell. Spiny softshells occur statewide in suitable habitat of perennial rivers that have sandy areas for nesting. Due to its rarity in South Dakota, the SDNHP monitors this species.

Habitat and Habits:

Spiny softshells use creeks, rivers, backwater areas, oxbows, lakes, and impoundments, although this is typically a riverine species. In South Dakota, spiny softshells prefer natural-flowing portions of the Missouri River and its larger tributaries. These turtles are also found in tributaries of the Minnesota River in northeastern South Dakota. Spiny softshells use rivers with soft bottoms, debris, and ample sandbars.

Spiny Softshell carapace   Al Gage

Front view of nostrils

Plastron   Al Gage

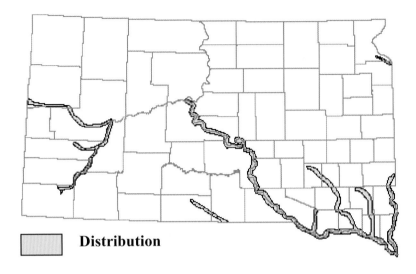

Distribution

Individuals are active during the day, spending most of their time in the water, like smooth softshells. Spiny softshells are more sedentary than smooth softshells. They often burrow into the bottom substrate or float near the water's surface, exposing only their head and/or nose. They also bask on sandy shores or within shallow waters. They overwinter buried beneath the substrate of rivers.

Mating begins in April and continues into May, with similar mating rituals and behavior as smooth softshells. Nest selection and preparation occur after a pair mates. The female excavates a nest up to 10 inches (25 cm) deep on sandbars and mudflats near water, depositing 12 to 18 brittle, spherical eggs. They may lay two clutches of eggs each year, one in late spring and another in late summer, much like smooth softshells. Eggs hatch in two to three months, with hatching usually occurring from late August to October. The sex of the embryos is genetically determined with a 1:1 sex ratio. This is also true of the smooth softshell, contrasted with other turtle species, where sex of embryos is temperature dependent.

Spiny softshells eat invertebrates, fish, and plant materials.

Remarks:

Spiny softshells are aggressive and difficult to handle. They stretch out their necks and attack by biting. They will also kick and scratch.

Like smooth softshells, spiny softshells can survive underwater for long periods because of their ability to respire using membranes within the mouth and cloaca.

This turtle is sometimes called the leatherback turtle.

Order Squamata

The order Squamata includes lizards and snakes. Members of this order have scales on the skin. The quadrate bone in members of this order has evolved such that it is loosely attached to the skull. This adaptation allows the back of the jaw to move more easily, allowing the mouth to open widely when they capture and handle prey. In particular, snakes have very flexible lower jaw and skull articulations that allow them to swallow large prey. Males in this order have a hemipenes, which is specific to this order. Male snakes locate females primarily by odor.

Family Phrynosomatidae

The family Phrynosomatidae includes earless, spiny, tree, side-blotched, and horned lizards. Some species have strongly-keeled scales. Most species in this family are terrestrial.

LESSER EARLESS LIZARD
Holbrookia maculata

Description:

This slender lizard measures 4 to 5 inches (10 to 13 cm) from head to tail as an adult. The tail is less than half of the total length. As the name implies, lesser earless lizards lack external ear openings.

Individuals vary in color and pattern. The tail, limbs, body, and head are uniformly light gray to gray-brown. The body has several brown or gray spots and sporadic bars. They have 8 to 14 circular dark spots on the back and pale stripes on the sides. The back is covered with small, flat, smooth scales. The white to light gray belly lacks spots and has large, overlapping, smooth scales.

Males are larger and have grayer throats than females. They also have pale striping and mottling on the back and two black bars enclosed in blue reaching to the armpits. During the breeding season, females have bright orange sides, most noticeable in the lateral striping.

Taxonomy/Distribution and Status:

The subspecies found in South Dakota is the northern earless lizard (*H. m. maculata*). Lesser earless lizards occur in the west central United States, typically in sandy, flat areas east of the Rockies. Lesser earless lizards reside mainly in sandy soils in south central and possibly southwestern South Dakota. Due to its rarity in South Dakota, the SDNHP monitors this species.

Habitat and Habits:

Lesser earless lizards select sandy areas with minimal vegetative cover in flat, open country, such as sandhill prairies, sandy grasslands, dry sandbars, and cultivated fields. They are active during the day, with daily activities including basking and foraging. During hot weather, they seek shelter beneath shady plants or within underground burrows. Temperatures above 70°F (21°C) are optimal for

Lesser Earless Lizard   Lauren J. Livo and Steve Wilcox

Lesser Earless Lizard   Colorado Division of Wildlife

lesser earless lizards.

These territorial lizards have a small home range, as with most lizards. Dominant males show their assertiveness by bobbing around or performing push-ups. Their mating rituals are similar to this dance of dominance.

Lesser earless lizards begin to mate in April after emerging from hibernation. A male nods its head, approaches a female, and pushes her on the side or beneath the tail. If receptive, she allows him to mount and copulate with her. Copulation begins once the cloacal openings align and ends within seconds.

Lesser earless lizards might produce two clutches per year, with the first clutch averaging four eggs. Eggs are deposited in May or June and hatch up to two months later. They use underground animal burrows during cool nights and as overwintering quarters.

They eat beetles and other arthropods.

Remarks:

Lesser earless lizards are nicknamed "sand puppies" or "sand dogs," since their long legs and toes allow them to run swiftly across sandy surfaces.

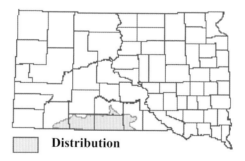

Distribution

SAGEBRUSH LIZARD
Sceloporus graciosus

Description:

Adult sagebrush lizards measure 5 to 6 inches (12 to 15 cm) from head to tail. They are pale brown, spiny lizards with few apparent markings. They have four rows of dark brown spots across the back, accented by two faint gray stripes. They also have one irregular dark spot on each shoulder and distinct wavy dark crossbands across the back. Sagebrush lizards have small, keeled, and pointed scales on the back and small, granular scales on the back of the thighs, which also have two black stripes separated by one light stripe. The individual in the photo is missing part of its tail, which it will regenerate.

Males have blue bellies, particularly along the sides, and little to no blue speckling on the throat, whereas females have white to faintly blue bellies and bright rusty sides at various stages of their reproductive cycle.

Taxonomy/Distribution and Status:

The subspecies found in South Dakota is the northern sagebrush lizard (*S. g. graciosus*). The species occurs in the western and west central United States, ranging from North Dakota and Nebraska to the Pacific Coast and from Montana to New Mexico. Sagebrush lizards occur in the southern and western regions of the Black Hills. Due to its rarity in South Dakota, the SDNHP monitors this species.

Habitat and Habits:

Sagebrush lizards inhabit dry, rocky areas in the southern and western portions of the Black Hills. They are active during the day and are primarily a ground-dwelling species, lingering near protective cover and perching on rocks or low-hanging branches.

Sagebrush lizards mate in the late spring. Their mating rituals are much like those of lesser earless lizards, where males dance to attract females (see lesser earless lizard account). A male attracts a receptive female and mounts her, followed by copulation. A female deposits approximately four eggs in early summer and may produce two clutches per year. Eggs hatch in August or September, and young sagebrush lizards reach adulthood at two years of age. They overwinter in underground burrows.

Sagebrush lizards eat insects and other arthropods.

Remarks:

Sagebrush lizards are common in drier shrub/steppe areas of the United States, but they are limited to localized populations in South Dakota.

Sagebrush Lizard   Doug Backlund

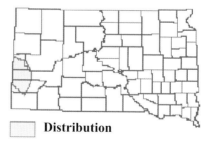

Distribution

PRAIRIE LIZARD
Sceloporus undulatus

Description:

Adult prairie lizards measure 4 to 7 inches (9 to 18 cm) from head to tail. The tail is more than half of the total length. Individuals are gray to brown with dark reddish brown sides. A light gray to brown line runs down the center of the back. The line is accented by two bold and distinct pale stripes and dark spots. Prairie lizards have large, rough-looking, keeled scales on the back. They also have overlapping, keeled scales on the backs of the thighs.

Males have two bright blue patches on the belly near the sides. This blue coloration rarely extends onto the throat. Females have white bellies without black speckling.

Taxonomy/Distribution and Status:

The subspecies found in South Dakota is the northern prairie lizard (*S. u. garmani*), which is smaller in size than other subspecies of prairie lizards. This species ranges from northern Mexico northward to South Dakota and westward to Utah and Arizona. In South Dakota, they occur in sandy regions with large areas of sand prairie and sand dunes. Prairie lizards are found in south central South Dakota west of the Missouri River, where populations appear stable. Due to its rarity in South Dakota, the SDNHP monitors this species.

Habitat and Habits:

Prairie lizards use sandy, open prairies with sufficient cover, including areas with yucca, shrubby flat areas, and wooded or rocky areas. Prairie lizards are known from sandhill areas associated with yucca in south central South Dakota. Although they occupy wooded or rocky areas, prairie lizards are uncoordinated climbers.

Prairie lizards are diurnal, when their activities include foraging and basking on rocks or logs. Activity peaks at temperatures above 70°F (21°C), but they avoid hot midday temperatures by seeking relief beneath plants or in underground burrows.

The territorial male has a harem of two to three females. They mate in early spring, usually in May. A male chases and mounts a receptive female. Copulation occurs when the cloacal openings align. The female prepares an underground nest in loose soil. She digs the nest in moist, sandy areas with temperatures ranging from 77°F to 84°F (25°C to 29°C). A female lays approximately seven eggs in late spring and may produce two to three clutches per year. Eggs hatch in two months. Prairie lizards overwinter in underground burrows.

Prairie lizards eat terrestrial arthropods such as beetles and grasshoppers.

Prairie Lizard   Doug Backlund

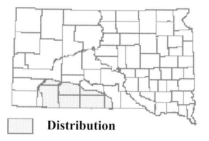

Distribution

Remarks:
    Prairie lizards have extremely brittle tails that may break off when a predator captures them by the tail. The tail will partly regenerate, but its length will not reach its original size.

SHORT-HORNED LIZARD
Phrynosoma hernandesi

Description:

Adult short-horned lizards range from 3 to 4 inches (6 to 10 cm) from head to tail. The broad body has a short tail and short, stumpy legs. The tail is less than a third of the total length. As the name implies, short-horned lizards have short horns covering the back and sides of their knoblike head. The horns are shorter than they are wide.

Short-horned lizards are gray to brown in color with dark, indistinct blotches across the back and spots or bands on the tail and limbs. The belly and underparts are white with some black mottling and flat, platelike scales. They have a single row of pigmented, fringed scales along the sides, and enlarged, keeled scales interspersed with granular scales on the back.

Taxonomy/Distribution and Status:

No subspecies is recognized in South Dakota. Short-horned lizards were previously known as eastern short-horned lizards (*P. douglasii brevirostre*) before the short-horned lizard was raised to the status of full species.

This species occupies suitable habitats of the west central United States, ranging from the Rocky Mountain states eastward as far as western South Dakota. The species is often difficult to detect and may be more abundant than indicated by surveys. Little historical information exists on short-horned lizards in South Dakota, although Patton described the species as common in Harding County in 1926 (Patton 1926). Due to its rarity in South Dakota, the SDNHP monitors this species.

Habitat and Habits:

This ground-dwelling lizard inhabits semiarid shortgrass or sage prairies with rocky or sandy areas and sparse vegetation. Short-horned lizards are active during the day.

They emerge in May or June, and mating begins. Females bear live young in mid- to late summer, giving birth to approximately 12 young each year. Individuals overwinter in underground burrows.

Short-horned lizards primarily eat ants, but will also prey on other arthropods.

Remarks:

When threatened, short-horned lizards may squirt blood from the corners of the eyes.

Short-horned Lizard

Doug Backlund

Distribution

Special References:

Patton, F. A. 1926. Our trip to the Eagle's nest. The Oologist 43:30.

Zamudio, K. R., K. B. Jones, and R. H. Ward. 1997. Molecular systematics of short-horned lizards: Biogeography and taxonomy of a widespread species complex. Systematic Biology 46:284-305.

Family Scincidae

The family Scincidae includes the skinks, which occur on all continents with temperate and tropical climates. Smooth, shiny scales cover their bodies. The brittle tail breaks off easily as a defense against predators. The tail will rejuvenate, but the newly-grown tail may be deformed and may not reach the same length as the original tail.

FIVE-LINED SKINK
Eumeces fasciatus

Description:

Adult five-lined skinks are 5 to 9 inches (13 to 22 cm) from head to tail. Juveniles are black, and adults are olive brown in color. Five-lined skinks have smooth, shiny, and round scales in horizontal rows. With the exception of older males, individuals have five blue-green to gray-tan lines across the back. As these skinks age, their color and patterns become more uniform, leaving older males with few markings or color variations on the back. They also have a line extending down the center of the back, forking near the tail. The five-lined skink has a gray belly and a pale cream-colored chin. Juveniles have bright blue tails, while adults have olive to gray tails. The male develops a red head and orange jaws during the breeding season.

Taxonomy/Distribution and Status:

No subspecies is recognized in South Dakota. Five-lined skinks are found from the southeastern to the central portions of eastern United States, particularly in damp, wooded areas. Stewart collected a five-lined skink in 1979 in Clay County, South Dakota, but there are no additional records of this species from the state (Backlund 2005). Due to its rarity in South Dakota, the SDNHP monitors this species.

Habitat and Habits:

Five-lined skinks are ground-dwelling, terrestrial reptiles that tend to burrow. They use damp habitats, such as woodlots with ample ground debris, including decaying leaves, sawdust piles, logs, and rocks, and/or patchy cover. Individuals hide beneath objects, such as rotting logs or stumps, or burrow into cracks in the ground regardless of the weather or temperature. They are active during the day and can be seen on warm, sunny days.

Five-lined skinks mate in the spring. The female deposits 7 to 13 eggs into nests typically "formed" in rotting logs or leaf litter. She protects her eggs by wrapping her body around them until they hatch in late July or early August. Five-lined skinks become sexually mature in two years. They overwinter in underground burrows.

This skink eats arthropods, such as grasshoppers and beetles.

Five-lined Skink   Jeffrey B. LeClere

Five-lined Skink (juvenile)   Jeffrey B. LeClere

MANY-LINED SKINK
Eumeces multivirgatus

Description:

Adult many-lined skinks measure 5 to 8 inches (13 to 19 cm) from head to tail. The tail is more than half of the total length. Individuals are light gray to dark brown with approximately ten stripes running the length of the back. These stripes alternate between dark and light brown; some stripes are obvious, and some are more subtle. Individuals have a broad, pale line in the center of the back that extends onto the head. This line forks into several different lines at the back of the head before extending onto the snout. Individuals in some populations may lack stripes. Juveniles are darker than adults and have a bright blue tail. Males have red lips during the breeding season.

The belly is light green to cream and lacks markings. Other characteristics include scale-covered eyelids, long tails, distinct ear openings, tubular bodies, and small, frail legs. Shiny, smooth, overlapping scales give these lizards a sleek appearance. The scales overlap in horizontal rows around the midsection.

Taxonomy/Distribution and Status:

The subspecies in South Dakota is the northern many-lined skink (*E. m. multivirgatus*). This subspecies is a regional endemic species in South Dakota, meaning it is native and unique to the region. Many-lined skinks live in the west central United States. They occur in the extreme southern to south central part of South Dakota. Historically, only two records were reported in the state. Six additional observations were reported in recent years in the south central part of South Dakota. Due to its rarity in South Dakota, the SDNHP monitors this species.

Habitat and Habits:

Many-lined skinks are ground-dwelling reptiles that inhabit sandy grasslands. Their body shape allows them to be fast runners in these grassland areas.

This secretive lizard is often found hiding beneath rocks, logs, or cow chips, where they seek shelter or search for food. Most individuals are active during the day, but hot weather may shift their activity to sunrise and sundown.

Many-lined skinks mate in early spring. Shortly after mating, the female lays two to seven eggs in a shallow nest. She protects her eggs until they hatch in July or August. Many-lined skinks likely overwinter in underground burrows.

Food items include various arthropods.

Remarks:

Many-lined skinks have brittle tails, which regenerate if broken off. The regenerated tail differs in color, texture, and length.

Many-lined Skink   Doug Backlund

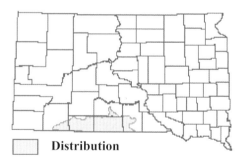

Distribution

PRAIRIE SKINK
Eumeces septentrionalis

Description:
   Adult prairie skinks measure 5 to 9 inches (13 to 22 cm) from head to tail. The tail is more than half of the total length. They are olive-gray, with two dark brown stripes separating three broad tan stripes on the back and a dark brown line separating two narrow pale lines on each side of the body. These lines are less apparent near the tip of the tail. The belly is bluish gray, and the chin is white with no markings. Prairie skinks are sleek looking because of their smooth, shiny, horizontal scales. They have white stripes on the backs of the thighs. Juveniles have bright blue tails. The sides of male's lower jaw and head become red during the breeding season.
   Prairie skinks are similar in appearance to many-lined skinks, but the pale striping on the sides of the body is restricted to the fourth and fifth row of scales, counting from the center of the back. This species has shorter legs than the many-lined skink.

Taxonomy/Distribution and Status:
   The subspecies recognized in South Dakota is the northern prairie skink (*E. s. septentrionalis*). Prairie skinks occur in the central United States in a small band stretching from Minnesota and North Dakota to Texas. This skink is found in the eastern fourth of South Dakota, where they are locally common.

Habitat and Habits:
   Prairie skinks inhabit grasslands that are relatively open and have loose soil and abundant cover. These secretive lizards seek shelter beneath rocks and logs or in underground burrows during extreme temperatures and/or for safety.
   Prairie skinks become active in early May and breed soon thereafter. The male mounts and copulates with a female. She digs a shallow nest in loose, moist soils near or within shelter and lays an average of nine eggs in late June or early July. She then guards and protects her eggs until they hatch in two months. Individuals reach sexual maturity at two years of age. They usually overwinter in burrows below the frost line to depths of up to 4.5 feet (1.4 m).
   They eat spiders and insects, especially grasshoppers.

Remarks:
   The prairie skink was once commonly called the black-banded skink because of the large dark brown bands along the sides of the body.

Prairie Skink   Dan Fogell

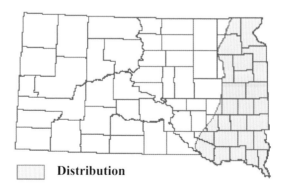

Distribution

Family Teiidae
The family Teiidae includes the whiptails and tegus, which occur in North and South America. Whiptails, also called racerunners, are North American representatives of the family Teiidae. Members of this family are diurnal, terrestrial lizards that have long tails and large scales along the back. Whiptails are insectivorous.

SIX-LINED RACERUNNER
Aspidoscelis sexlineata

Description:
Adult six-lined racerunners measure 6 to 11 inches (15 to 27 cm) from head to tail. They are slender lizards, and the tail comprises approximately half the total length. They are brown to dark green in color, with the front part of the body appearing green to blue, particularly in males. Seven light green, blue, yellow, or white lines stretch from the head to the tail, with one line running through the center of the back and three lines running along the sides. Six-lined racerunners have a noticeable bright green wash over these lines on the front third of their body, including the head. Juveniles have a distinctive blue tail.

Six-lined racerunners have tiny, round scales on the back and eight rows of large, rectangular scales on the belly. Other characteristics include a pointed nose, yellow irises, a rough gray tail and limbs, an olive green head, and a lack of spots on the body.

The male has a light blue chin and lips during the breeding season. Males also have white to bluish-white unmarked bellies. Females have salmon pink to creamy white bellies.

Taxonomy/Distribution and Status:
The subspecies found in South Dakota is the prairie racerunner (*A. s. viridis*). This species was formerly in the genus *Cnemidophorus*. Based on recent research, *Cnemidophorus* was reclassified as *Aspidoscelis*. This species is found in the south central and southeastern United States. The northern limit of its range includes southern South Dakota, southeastern Minnesota, and southwestern Wisconsin. Six-lined racerunners occupy sandy areas, such as sandhills of southwestern and south central South Dakota. Due to its rarity in South Dakota, the SDNHP monitors this species.

Habitat and Habits:
Six-lined racerunners use dry, sandy, open areas with sparse vegetation. These areas may be along riverbanks or floodplains, in grasslands, in sagebrush areas, or near rocky outcroppings. Individuals are terrestrial and diurnal. Like most teiids, six-lined racerunners prefer air temperatures greater than 90°F.

Six-lined racerunners are fast runners and accomplished burrowers. They often seek shelter in underground burrows or under objects during cold weather

Six-lined Racerunner   Lauren J. Livo and Steve Wilcox

or to escape danger

Although not territorial, they occupy a home range. They mate after emerging in the spring, usually in May or June. A male attracts a female by displaying his colorful chin and chest. A receptive female allows a displaying male to grab her loose throat skin and mount her. The female digs a nest up to 4 inches (10 cm) deep in a sandy area and lays an average of three eggs. Eggs hatch in approximately two months, usually in August. Young racerunners can mate the following year. Two-year-old females may produce two clutches per season. Six-lined racerunners overwinter in underground burrows.

This species uses hearing and smell to capture food. They feed primarily on arthropods, such as grasshoppers, beetles, and spiders.

Remarks:

Six-lined racerunners are nicknamed "fieldstreaks" or "sandlappers" because of their agility and dartlike speed.

Special References:

Reeder, T. W., C. J. Cole, and H.C. Dessauer. 2002. Phylogenetic relationships of whiptail lizards of the genus *Cnemidophorus* (Squamata: Teiidae): A test of monophyly, reevaluation of karyotypic evolution, and review of hybrid origins. American Museum Novitates 3365:1-61.

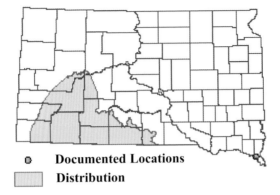

Documented Locations
Distribution

Family Colubridae

Members of this family have large teeth in the rear of the mouth. Many species in this family have a Duvernoy's gland, which produces secretions composed of enzymes or venoms. These secretions aid in the capture or digestion of prey. Some species are nonvenomous. Other species possess weak venom that allows them to subdue and begin digesting prey. Still others are highly venomous and have the potential to invenomate prey and people. In South Dakota, none of the species in this family is dangerous to people. South Dakota snakes that are not venomous to people have round pupils, unlike the prairie rattlesnake, which is venomous to people and has elliptical pupils.

RACER
Coluber constrictor

Description:

Adult racers are slender snakes measuring 23 to 50 inches (58 to 127 cm) from head to tail. Juveniles have chestnut to black spots on their back, sides, and belly. They develop adult coloration in two to three years. Adults have a greenish-blue back and a plain cream to white belly. Racers have white chin patches, large eyes, and smooth, shiny scales. They also have divided anal plates and nostrils that exit between two scales. Males have longer tails and are slightly smaller than females.

Taxonomy/Distribution and Status:

The subspecies in South Dakota is the eastern yellow-bellied racer (*C. c. flaviventris*). Racers occur throughout the United States east of the Rocky Mountains and west of the Rocky Mountains in lower lying plains. The racer is one of the most common snakes of the northern Great Plains. Racers occur in grasslands in western and central South Dakota.

Habitat and Habits:

Racers use open grasslands and pastures that provide adequate cover, such as clumps of vegetation, small mammal burrows, and rock piles. They tend to select drier grassy areas but also may inhabit open forested regions. Racers commonly inhabit areas near wetlands.

Racers occupy a home range but are not territorial. They are agile and fast in the face of danger. Although primarily terrestrial, they may swim or climb to heights of up to 12 inches (30 cm).

Racers are active from May and October, and they mate in May or June. Males find females by scent. After locating a receptive female, the male moves his body over hers until she becomes passive, and copulation occurs.

The female lays 8 to 21 eggs in underground burrows or beneath logs in June or July. The number of eggs laid depends on the size of the female. Eggs hatch in two to three months. Racers overwinter in underground dens, such as

Adult Racer   Dan Fogell

Juvenile Racer   Dan Fogell

burrows or caves, sometimes occupying the same dens as prairie rattlesnakes and milksnakes.

They swallow prey alive without constricting them. Racers eat small mammals, birds, and insects. A racer at Wind Cave National Park was found with a belly full of grasshoppers.

Remarks:

The racer is commonly called the "blue racer" because of its color. When they become alarmed, the tail begins vibrating. If captured, they will bite, struggle, and discharge musk and waste from the vent.

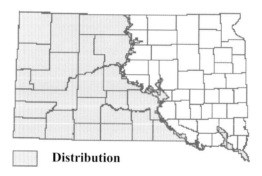

Distribution

RING-NECKED SNAKE
Diadophis punctatus

Description:
Adult ring-necked snakes measure 10 to 14 inches (25 to 36 cm) from head to tail. Their distinct yellow-orange ring, bordered in black, stretches around the neck. The neck ring may be interrupted. Ring-necked snakes are reddish brown to brownish black and have a black mottled, bright yellow to orange belly. The underside of the tail is bright red. Ring-necked snakes also have smooth scales and divided anal plates. Juveniles are generally shinier and darker than adults. Females are larger than males.

Taxonomy/Distribution and Status:
The subspecies recognized in South Dakota is the prairie ring-necked snake *(D. p. arnyi)*. Ring-necked snakes range throughout the United States, except for the arid West region. They occur in extreme southeastern South Dakota, where they are primarily associated with woodlands and prairie hillsides along the Missouri and Big Sioux rivers. The species has also been reported and observed in Brule County. Due to its rarity in South Dakota, the SDNHP monitors this species.

Habitat and Habits:
Ring-necked snakes are associated with woodland edges, prairie uplands, and hilly pastures near wetlands. They are rather shy and secretive snakes that are primarily active during the night. They require ground cover, such as logs, rocks, or boards, in moist areas during the day. They are rarely seen basking in the sun, and in periods of hot, dry weather they use underground burrows for protection.

Ring-necked snakes are active from April to October, which is typical of snakes in South Dakota. They mate in early spring, when males mount females and copulate. She lays eggs in June or July in a nest located in an underground burrow, rotting logs, or under rocks in moist areas. Females deposit an average of four eggs per clutch, although clutch size depends on the female's body size. Ring-necked snakes sometimes form nesting colonies. Eggs hatch up to two months after deposition. Ring-necked snakes become sexually mature at two to three years of age, depending on the sex. They overwinter underground beneath the frost line.

These snakes are not venomous to people. They use their sense of smell to locate prey, which consists of earthworms, small snakes, frogs, and soft-bodied insects.

Dorsal surface of Ring-necked Snake   Dan Fogell

Ventral surface   Dan Fogell

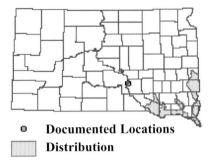

◉ **Documented Locations**

▦ **Distribution**

Remarks:

Ring-necked snakes are docile, but they release an anal musk and coil the tail when threatened with danger. By coiling its tail, it tries to display the tail's red underside. They are called "corkscrew" or "thimble" snakes due to their coiling and lifting actions.

WESTERN FOXSNAKE
Elaphe vulpina

Description:
Adult western foxsnakes measure 36 to 54 inches (91 to 137 cm) from head to tail. They are well camouflaged with a yellowish brown back mottled with dark brown blotches. The yellowish-white belly is speckled with black rectangular blotches.

The western foxsnake has a brownish head with few distinct markings and a wide, sharp nose. They have large spots across the center of the back and small spots across the sides of the back. They also have a divided anal plate and slightly keeled scales in the middle of the back.

Juveniles are slightly lighter than adults, with more distinct body markings. Juveniles are gray with brown, black-bordered spots. As they reach adulthood, their color darkens and their markings fade. Juveniles also have different lines on the forehead, through the eyes, and near the mouth. They may also have black specks along the upper lip.

Taxonomy/Distribution and Status:
Foxsnakes are found in the north central United States. The subspecies found in South Dakota is the western foxsnake (*E. v. vulpina*). They occur in the extreme southeastern portion of South Dakota. Due to its rarity in South Dakota, the SDNHP monitors this species.

Habitat and Habits:
Foxsnakes live in open prairies and stream valleys near woody areas. They are active during daylight hours and rest during the night beneath objects such as rocks or logs.

Foxsnakes are active from April to October, and they mate in early spring. Courtship begins when a male pursues a female. Once a receptive female remains motionless, the male moves alongside her and begins probing her head while twitching his tongue. Both animals begin to shudder, signaling him to mount her. He then wraps his tail around hers to copulate while using his mouth to grab her at the back of her head.

Females nest beneath leaf litter or within stumps or logs. They lay 8 to 27 eggs, which hatch in about three months. Foxsnakes overwinter beneath the frost line in such areas as underground burrows.

Foxsnakes are not venomous to people, but they will vibrate their tail, coil their body, and strike when approached.

Food items include small mammals, eggs, and birds. They use constriction to subdue live prey.

Western Foxsnake   Dan Fogell

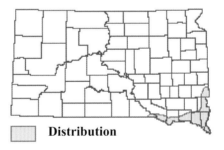

Distribution

Remarks:

Foxsnakes have feeding habits that are economically important to farmers. They are often mistaken for gophersnakes (or bullsnakes). The gophersnake has an undivided anal plate, while the foxsnake has a divided anal plate. The foxsnake also does not hiss, as does the gophersnake.

Foxsnakes are occasionally collected for the pet trade. Their name may be derived from their distinctive anal musk smell, which is similar to the smell of the red fox.

WESTERN HOG-NOSED SNAKE
Heterodon nasicus

Description:

Adult western hog-nosed snakes measure 15 to 25 inches (38 to 64 cm) from head to tail. As the name implies, the western hog-nosed snake has a markedly upturned snout with a sharp point and central ridge.

This snake has a pale yellowish-brown body with three rows of dark brown or olive spots extending from the head to the tail. The head has a dark blotchy line stretching from one corner of the mouth through each eye to the opposite corner of the mouth. They have a white throat and a black belly with yellow mottling. The head is covered in finely-grained scales. The scales covering the body are strongly keeled. The underside of the tail and belly is black, and the divided anal plate has a hint of yellow. Juveniles are lighter in color and have more distinct patterning than adults. Females are usually larger than males and have shorter tails and more spots across the back.

See the eastern hog-nosed snake account for tips on distinguishing between these two species.

Taxonomy/Distribution and Status:

The subspecies recognized in South Dakota is the plains hog-nosed snake (*H. n. nasicus*). Western hog-nosed snakes range throughout the central plains of the United States and southern Canada. This species is found statewide, but is most common in western South Dakota.

Habitat and Habits:

Western hog-nosed snakes generally use open prairies or sandy areas near floodplains and water. Although they select areas near water, they burrow in grasslands in sandy areas with well-drained soils. This snake is adapted for bur-rowing, as indicated by the upturned snout. Using its nose as a shovel, the snake burrows by moving from side to side.

This snake is active from May to September, with the greatest activity in the morning and early evening hours. They mate in the spring and occasionally in the fall. Approximately one month after copulation, the female lays nine eggs in an excavated nest located in damp soil several centimeters below the surface. Eggs hatch in two to three months.

Western hog-nosed snakes seek underground shelter in extremely hot or cold temperatures. They overwinter in burrows beneath the frost line.

This snake is not venomous to people, but the saliva is toxic to prey and can be painful to humans. Enlarged teeth in the rear upper jaw are used to inject toxins and to deflate toads. Duvernoy's glands are paired glands associated with the upper jaws of colubrids. Secretions from this gland immobilize prey by acting like a toxin. They feed primarily on toads, but they also eat other amphibians, lizards, small mammals, and ground-nesting birds.

Western Hog-nosed Snake   Doug Backlund

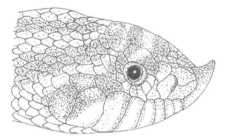

The snout is more strongly upturned than that of the
Eastern Hog-nosed Snake.

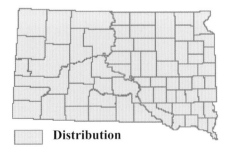

Distribution

Remarks:

The western hog-nosed snake is also known as the "prairie rooter." They may be mistaken as venomous snakes because they tend to flare the bones at the rear angle of the jaw, giving a slightly triangular look to the head. They may strike if frightened, and their bite can cause swelling and discoloration of the skin at the site of the bite. Their typical defensive behavior involves loud hissing sounds with closed-mouth strikes. Eventually, they simulate death by vomiting and eliminating from the cloaca, rolling on their back, and exposing their belly while in the coiled position. The snake may also open its mouth while in the belly-up position.

This species is captured for the pet trade.

EASTERN HOG-NOSED SNAKE
Heterodon platirhinos

Description:

Adult eastern hog-nosed snakes average larger than western hog-nosed snakes, measuring 20 to 33 inches (51 to 84 cm) from head to tail. Unlike the western hog-nosed snake, this species has an indistinctly-upturned snout, which is nearly straight in profile.

A pair of large, dark blotches mark the back of the head. Eastern hog-nosed snakes may be yellow, orange, reddish-brown, olive, or dark gray. The center and sides of the back and tail have irregular dark spots. The belly is mottled gray, yellow, or pink, with light tail underparts. Other characteristics include keeled dorsal scales, divided anal plates, and a light chin and throat. Juveniles have more distinct patterning on the back and indistinct patterning on the belly compared to adults. Females are often larger than males. In certain areas, some individuals are jet black or plain gray in color. This unique coloration has been reported in South Dakota.

The underside of the western hog-nosed snake's tail and belly are black. The eastern hog-nosed snake has a dark belly, and the underside of the tail is much lighter than the belly.

Taxonomy/Distribution and Status:

No subspecies is recognized in South Dakota. Eastern hog-nosed snakes are found throughout the eastern United States. This species is sparsely distributed throughout its range. In South Dakota, the eastern hog-nosed snake is found primarily in extreme southeastern counties along the Missouri River. Due to its rarity in South Dakota, the SDNHP monitors this species.

Habitat and Habits:

Eastern hog-nosed snakes select open wooded areas near water, although the areas are less open than those used by western hog-nosed snakes. Other habitats include sandy plains near major rivers, old fields, and grasslands. They are documented in sandy regions adjacent to cottonwood forests along the Missouri River.

Much like western hog-nosed snakes, this snake uses its nose to burrow into the ground or take advantage of shelter beneath objects, such as rocks or logs. These snakes are active from April to October and mate in April or May.

Little is known about the mating habits of eastern hog-nosed snakes, although a male will follow a female for several days while constantly flicking his tongue. The male and female separate after copulation. She digs a nest in a sandy area where she lays an average of 22 eggs. Eggs hatch in June or July after two months of incubation. Eastern hog-nosed snakes usually produce one clutch each year. They overwinter in deep burrows, which they dig in the soil or sand deeply enough to avoid cold temperatures.

Eastern Hog-nosed Snake   Dan Fogell

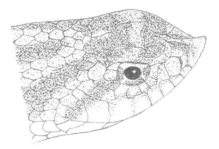

The snout is less obviously upturned than that of
the Western Hog-nosed Snake.

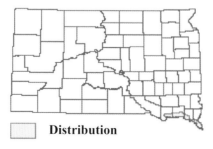

Distribution

112

These snakes are docile. The enlarged upper jaw teeth help them grab prey and deflate toads. Prey includes toads, frogs, and salamanders.

Remarks:

Eastern hog-nosed snakes play possum much like western hog-nosed snakes. Nicknames of this snake include "spreading adder" and "puff adder."

Special References:

Kirsch, S. 1983. Ecology of the eastern hognose snake in southeastern South Dakota. M.A. Thesis. University of South Dakota, Vermillion, South Dakota. 42pp.

MILKSNAKE
Lampropeltis triangulum

Description:

Adult milksnakes measure 21 to 28 inches (53 to 71 cm) from head to tail. The body is slender and red to orange. The back has yellow markings bordered in black, giving this snake a banded appearance. Two subspecies occur in South Dakota, the pale and red milksnakes. The pale milksnake is orange to grayish brown with pale gray, yellow, or cream-colored alternating bands. The head is orange, and the snout is speckled with black. The red milksnake is grayish-white or yellow with large brown to reddish brown markings across the back and sides. They have white to yellow collars, red heads, and red snouts.

Milksnakes have variable color patterns on the belly, which help distinguish subspecies. The pale milksnake has a white belly with minimal markings that form a shape resembling the letter "H." The red milksnake's belly is checkered with black and white squarelike markings.

Due to their patterning and coloration, milksnakes resemble coral snakes. However, milksnakes are harmless, and coral snakes do not occur in South Dakota. The saying, "red touch yellow kill a fellow, red touch black good for jack," is commonly used to distinguish between milksnakes and coral snakes, referring to the band patterns. Milksnakes have a single anal plate and flat scales. Males are typically larger than females.

Taxonomy/Distribution and Status:

Two subspecies are recognized in South Dakota, the pale milksnake (*L. t. multistriata*) and red milksnake (*L. t. syspila*). The pale milksnake is known as the "house snake" in some areas because they may inhabit buildings. Red milksnakes are also known as "red snakes" or "candy cane snakes" in some areas and as "corn snakes" in other areas due to their characteristic yellowish back, which resembles a cornhusk. However, the true corn snake (*Elaphe guttata*) is a different species that is not found in South Dakota.

Milksnakes have one of the largest ranges of any snake, ranging across much of the eastern United States to the Rocky Mountains. Pale milksnakes occur in the northern central plains, while red milksnakes are found in the southeastern United States. Pale milksnakes are found west of the Missouri River in South Dakota, while red milksnakes are found in southeastern South Dakota.

Habitat and Habits:

Milksnakes use grassland and forested habitats, sand dunes, high plains to rocky hillsides, and woodlands. These secretive snakes usually seek shelter or warmth beneath objects, such as rocks or wood, rather than basking in the sun.

They are usually active during the night from April to October, and they mate sometime between April and June. During copulation, the male bites the female on the neck to grasp her, which is fairly common snake behavior.

Milksnake   Dan Fogell

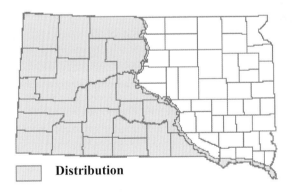

□ **Distribution**

115

The female lays an average of five to seven eggs under rocks or in burrows. Eggs are often deposited one to two months after copulation. The young leave the nest in late August or early September. Milksnakes overwinter in rock outcrops, burrows, and building foundations.

They constrict prey after seizing it, and prey eventually dies of suffocation. Milksnakes primarily eat small mammals and may take lizards, other snakes, small birds, and eggs.

Remarks:

As is true of most snakes, milksnakes coil and vibrate their tail when startled. They may occasionally strike and bite fiercely or hide their head beneath the coiled tail. They are not venomous.

The name milksnake is derived from folklore, when milksnakes were thought to milk cows.

Because of the beautiful coloration of these snakes, milksnakes are commonly found in the pet trade and sometimes collected illegally.

NORTHERN WATERSNAKE
Nerodia sipedon

Description:

Adult northern watersnakes reach lengths of 24 to 42 inches (61 to 107 cm) from head to tail. They are brown to gray and often darker as adults than as juveniles. The head and front of the body have irregular dark gray to reddish brown bands. These bands become large blotches on the back and alternate with small blotches on the sides, sometimes becoming distinct bands along the tail. Individuals darken with age, causing the patterning on the back to disappear, but this pattern remains visible in the water.

Northern watersnakes have black-bordered, reddish crescents on the belly, which eventually become darker at the end of the belly and onto the underpart of the tail. These crescents may be indistinct, distinct, or absent. Other characteristics include a divided anal plate, keeled lateral and dorsal scales, a blunt nose, and a cream-colored chin.

Males are smaller but have longer tails than females.

Taxonomy/Distribution and Status:

The subspecies recognized in South Dakota is the northern watersnake (*N. s. sipedon*). This species is associated with major drainages in the east central United States. In South Dakota, museum records exist only from Bon Homme County. This snake is limited to the Missouri River near Springfield, South Dakota, where there may be a small population. Due to its rarity in South Dakota, the SDNHP monitors this species.

Habitat and Habits:

Northern watersnakes inhabit permanent lakes and rivers that have fish. These wetlands are usually in quiet areas with little pollution.

This snake is active from April to October, being active during the day in cool weather and shifting to nightly activity in warm weather. Northern watersnakes are generally more active in cool weather than are most snakes. They bask on tree or shrub branches, logs, or rocks near or above the water, often fleeing danger by diving into the water.

They mate in the spring in water or on land. A male locates a female via scent. He rubs her along her neck while jerking his body, stimulating her to mate. He then wraps his tail around hers before copulation. An average 20 to 25 young are born in August or September, three to four months after breeding. Young are born alive within a thin transparent membrane. Northern watersnakes overwinter in crevices or holes in hillsides and in crayfish burrows in lowland areas.

They eat fish, frogs, and salamanders.

Northern Watersnake

Dan Fogell

□ **Documented Locations**

Remarks:

When alarmed, this snake flattens itself and bites violently while twisting its body and releasing anal musk to help deter threats. As a last defense mechanism, this snake will bite. Although northern watersnakes are not venomous, they are often mistaken as venomous water moccasins in some parts of their range.

118

SMOOTH GREEN SNAKE
Liochlorophis vernalis

Description:

Adult smooth green snakes are small, thin snakes that measure 12 to 20 inches (30 to 51 cm) from head to tail. They are uniformly green across the back. The belly varies from white to yellow and lacks markings. Smooth scales and a long narrow mouth give this snake a sleek appearance. Other characteristics include a divided anal plate and a bright red tongue tipped with black.

The color of this snake often changes to blue upon death, causing them to be confused with racers. Large smooth green snakes are also sometimes confused with racers. Adult smooth green snakes are usually the size of juvenile racers, and juvenile racers are marked differently than smooth green snakes (see racer account).

Taxonomy/Distribution and Status:

No subspecies is recognized in South Dakota due to the lack of differences among populations. Smooth green snakes range across the northern tier of states and in adjacent southern Canada, west of the Great Plains. Isolated populations are found across the Great Plains and in the western United States. This species is found in the Black Hills and in northeastern and southeastern South Dakota. Due to its rarity in South Dakota, the SDNHP monitors this species.

Habitat and Habits:

Smooth green snakes primarily use moist grassy areas in meadows and prairies in woodlands, although they sometimes wander far from water. Although these snakes are largely terrestrial and semifossorial, they show a slight tendency to climb, occasionally climbing in shrubs to feed and bask. They seek shelter beneath objects such as rocks and logs. Occasionally, they can be found on roads early on summer mornings.

The smooth green snake is most active from April to September in the early morning and late afternoon. They mate in May, although little is known about the mating habits of this species. The female lays 3 to 11 eggs in July or August in tree hollows or in decaying logs or vegetation. Eggs hatch approximately one month later. The females can hold growing eggs in her abdomen several weeks before they hatch, as indicated by short egg development periods.

These nonvenomous snakes seize and swallow their prey whole without constriction. Their food consists of invertebrates, such as spiders, insects, and slugs.

Remarks:

This snake is also known as the "green grass snake." They rarely strike, but they may open their mouths exposing the white inside of the mouth to would-be predators.

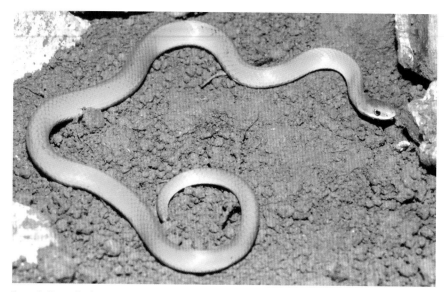

Smooth Green Snake   Dan Fogell

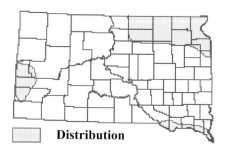

Distribution

GOPHERSNAKE
Pituophis catenifer

Description:
Gophersnakes are commonly known as bullsnakes. Adults range from 37 to 72 inches (95 to 183 cm) from head to tail. This is the largest snake in South Dakota.

The yellowish back is covered with dark brown rectangular spots that alternate with blotches on the sides. These blotches stretch onto the cream-colored belly. These markings are darker and more distinct on the head and tail.

Black bars cut vertically across the upper lip, and black and yellow alternating lines extend from the eye to the angle of the jaw. A wedge-shaped scale rests on the top edge of the nose. Gophersnakes have strongly keeled scales and a single anal plate.

Taxonomy/Distribution and Status:
Gophersnakes are found throughout much of the central and western United States. The subspecies found in South Dakota is the bullsnake (*P. c. sayi*). *P. c. sayi* ranges throughout the Great Plains of southern Canada and the United States. Gophersnakes are common throughout South Dakota, except for the northeastern region.

Habitat and Habits:
Gophersnakes inhabit grasslands. They may also inhabit woodland areas and river bluffs. This snake is active from May to September. During the warmer months, they are most active during the early morning and night. They often seek shelter in clumps of vegetation, beneath objects such as rocks, or in burrows during hot days.

They mate in the early spring, usually in May. After a two- to three-month incubation period, the female lays an average of 13 eggs in a mammal burrow, log, or loose sandy soil. Eggs hatch in two to three months.

Gophersnakes are constrictors. Small mammals and birds are common prey. They will also eat eggs.

Remarks:
Gophersnakes first attempt to flee rather than aggressively defend themselves. If cornered, they hiss loudly while shaking their tail, thus mimicking prairie rattlesnakes. The two species are frequently confused with each other. Gophersnakes benefit people because they prey on crop-destroying rodents.

Gophersnake (Bullsnake)   Dan Fogell

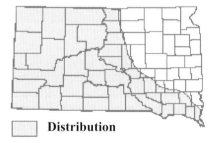

Distribution

122

BROWNSNAKE
Storeria dekayi

Description:
Adult brownsnakes range from 9 to 13 inches (23 to 33 cm) from head to tail. They are brown, gray, or reddish brown and have parallel rows of dark blotches with narrow upward extensions. A thick, gray line in the center of the back may link to these blotches by the upward extensions. They also have indistinct spots on the sides of the body that alternate with the blotches. The middle of the back appears lighter than the sides. Brownsnakes have a pale yellow, brown, or pink belly with minimal markings. The belly scales have one or two tiny dark blotches. They have dark lines behind the eyes and dark spots beneath the eyes, behind the head, and along the neck. Brownsnakes have keeled scales and a divided anal plate. Juveniles are darker than adults and have a yellow ring around the neck. Males have longer tails and smaller bodies than females.

Taxonomy/Distribution and Status:
The subspecies found in South Dakota is the Texas brownsnake (*S. d. texana*). Brownsnakes are found in wetland and terrestrial habitats in the eastern United States. The subspecies that occurs in South Dakota is found in the central United States from Minnesota and South Dakota to Texas.

There is currently only one record of this snake known from South Dakota. It was collected in Roberts County in 1922. Due to its rarity in South Dakota, the SDNHP monitors this species.

Habitat and Habits:
Brownsnakes use moist habitats, such as freshwater marshes, moist woods, and grasslands. Little is known about their habitat use in South Dakota due to the lack of sightings.

These secretive snakes spend much of their time hiding beneath objects, such as rocks, logs, or boards. Brownsnakes are generally active from April to early fall.

Brownsnakes mate in the early spring after a male locates a receptive female through scent. The female gives birth to an average of 14 young three to four months after copulation. Young are born alive within a thin transparent membrane. Brownsnakes overwinter underground below the frost line.

They seek out prey through scent. Food items include slugs, snails, soft-bodied insect larvae, and earthworms.

Remarks:
Brownsnakes are docile snakes that rarely bite. When alarmed, they flatten their bodies and release an anal musk.

The brownsnake was previously called the DeKay's snake, named after the 19th century New York naturalist, James Edward DeKay.

Brownsnake

Dan Fogell

REDBELLY SNAKE
Storeria occipitomaculata

Description:
Adults ranges from 8 to 10 inches (20 to 25 cm) from head to tail. Redbelly snakes are gray, brown, or reddish brown and have a distinct red to pink belly. Four faint brown stripes run down the back, with one thick, lighter stripe through the center of the back. The top of the head is darker than the top of the body.

The redbelly snake has a white chin and three yellow markings along the neck, which may be absent in some populations or specimens. Yellow neck spots on Black Hills redbelly snakes are usually absent or indistinct. Northern redbelly snakes in eastern South Dakota have yellow neck spots that are usually present and quite distinct. Black Hills redbelly snakes also have a very faint line on the adjacent edges of the second and third scale rows counting from the belly up. They have keeled scales and a divided anal plate.

Juveniles are darker than adults and have an indistinct red or pink belly and a yellow neck collar, characteristics that are absent in adults. Females are larger and have shorter tails than males.

Taxonomy/Distribution and Status:
The two subspecies recognized in South Dakota are the Black Hills redbelly snake (*S. o. pahasapae*) and the northern redbelly snake (*S. o. occipitomaculata*). The Black Hills redbelly snake was originally named and described by Smith (1963). Redbelly snakes are found throughout the eastern United States and may be quite common in some areas. Northern redbelly snakes are found in eastern South Dakota. Black Hills redbelly snakes occur in the Black Hills of South Dakota, where it is one of the few endemic taxa found in this region. They are distributed throughout the Black Hills, particularly in riparian areas where prey, such as snails and slugs, is abundant. Due to its rarity in South Dakota, the SDNHP monitors this species.

Habitat and Habits:
Redbelly snakes inhabit woodlands and moist grassy areas, usually near water. They are secretive snakes, spending most of their time hidden beneath objects such as rocks, fallen logs, and debris piles, within grass, or beneath shrubs, especially during hot weather. Because of their secretive behavior, they are difficult to detect.

In the Black Hills, redbelly snakes are active from May to October. It is also suggested that these snakes are associated with open wet meadows and immature deciduous forest, such as quaking aspen stands.

They court and mate in the spring or sometimes in the summer or fall. They bear an average of eight young in August or September. If they mate in the summer or fall, females can delay fertilization by storing sperm through the winter, and young are born in the spring. Redbelly snakes reach sexual maturity by the

125

Black Hills Redbelly Snake   Scott Weins

Black Hills Redbelly Snake   Doug Backlund

126

age of two years. They overwinter in underground sites similar to those used by brownsnakes, such as ant mounds, foundations, or wells.

They eat snails, slugs, earthworms, and insect larvae.

Remarks:

Redbelly snakes are docile and behave much like brownsnakes when alarmed. They release an anal musk and may flare their lips to display their teeth. They also have been observed to play dead, much like hog-nosed snakes, by exposing their red bellies.

Special References:

Smith, H. M. 1963. The identity of the Black Hills population of *Storeria occipotomaculata*, the red-bellied snake. Herpetologica 19:16-21.

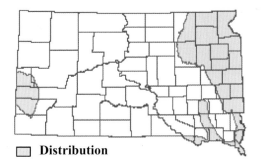

☐ **Distribution**

Terrestrial Gartersnake
Thamnophis elegans

Description:
Adult terrestrial gartersnakes measure 18 to 30 inches (46 to 76 cm) from head to tail. Color ranges from brown to greenish-brown to gray, and the belly is often pale gray. One faint whitish stripe stretches down the center of the back, and one faint stripe stretches along each side of the body. Between each line are alternating rows of dark, circular markings. This snake has black markings speckled along the edges of the belly. They can be very dark and almost melanistic. The brown head is speckled with yellow, and the throat is creamy white. They also have black bars on the lips. This species has keeled scales and an undivided anal plate. Males are usually smaller and have longer tails than females.

Taxonomy/Distribution and Status:
The subspecies recognized in South Dakota is the wandering gartersnake (*T. e. vagrans*). These snakes range throughout mountainous areas of the western United States. In South Dakota, they are found at higher elevations in the Black Hills, usually above 4,500 feet. They were recently documented in northwestern South Dakota in the North Cave Hills and in sandy areas near streams in Harding County.

Habitat and Habits:
Terrestrial gartersnakes exploit a variety of habitats. Like all gartersnakes, they are most frequently encountered near water in relatively sandy areas but are less likely to be found near water than are other members of this genus. They are also found at higher elevations than many gartersnake species.

They are active during the day from May to September in the Black Hills area. Courtship behavior begins as they emerge from hibernation. Males emerge earlier than females and usually begin courtship behavior in response to environmental changes. The female releases a special scent through her skin to attract mates. A male follows this scent by trailing the female prior to mating. The female gives birth to an average of 8 to 12 snakes each year.

Terrestrial gartersnakes have a diverse diet, including fish, frogs, slugs, leeches, and earthworms.

Remarks:
Like all gartersnakes, if captured and held, terrestrial gartersnakes struggle and release a strong-smelling musk.

Terrestrial Gartersnake   Doug Backlund

Distribution

Plains Gartersnake
Thamnophis radix

Description:

Adult plains gartersnakes measure 15 to 28 inches (38 to 71 cm) from head to tail, so their size is similar to the terrestrial gartersnake. One bright yellow to orange line runs down the spine, and one pale yellow line runs along each side. Plains gartersnakes have stripes on scale rows three and four, counting from the belly up. Two rows of alternating black dots or squares are found between these stripes. The belly ranges in color from whitish to pale green. The edges of the belly have dark markings. They have dark heads and pale green upper lips. The upper lip also has black vertical bars. They have strongly keeled scales and an undivided anal plate.

The plains gartersnake can be distinguished from the terrestrial gartersnake by its overall lighter appearance and presence of more striking lines. It can be distinguished from the common gartersnake by this species' lack of red checkered coloration and the slightly orange tint to the central stripe. Adult males have longer tails and are smaller than adult females.

Taxonomy/Distribution and Status:

The subspecies found in South Dakota is the western plains gartersnake (*T. r. haydenii*). Plains gartersnakes are found in the Great Plains of North America from northern Texas to southern Canada. They are common throughout South Dakota.

Habitat and Habits:

Plains gartersnakes typically inhabit grassy or shrubby areas bordering wetlands, but they can also range relatively far from water. These snakes are usually active during the day from mid-April to November, depending on the weather, but they can be commonly observed on roads on warm evenings.

They usually mate in the spring, from mid-April to early May, but they may also mate in the fall. Females attract males much like other gartersnakes (see terrestrial gartersnake account). If they mate in the fall, the female can delay egg fertilization until the following spring. She gives birth to an average of 25 young in late August or early September. Plains gartersnakes often den communally with other snakes in abandoned mammal burrows, ant mounds, building foundations, or old wells.

Their diet is diverse. They primarily prey on amphibians but they also eat fish, insects, small mammals, and earthworms.

Plains Gartersnake   Doug Backlund

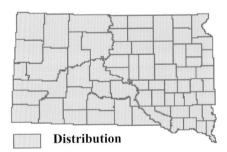

Distribution

Remarks:

    Plains gartersnakes, much like terrestrial gartersnakes, can be quite active while they are in hand, often releasing musk as a defense mechanism. They also may bite when handled.

    This species has been observed to coil its body, hiding the head beneath the body slowly waving the tail in what appears to be an anti-predator behavior.

COMMON GARTERSNAKE
Thamnophis sirtalis

Description:

Adult common gartersnakes measure 16 to 26 inches (41 to 66 cm) from head to tail. They are slightly different in coloration than other gartersnakes in South Dakota, being dark olive to dark brown with a gray to green belly. They have one bright yellow stripe down the back and one sharply-edged yellow, orange, green, or blue line along each of the sides. These two lines occur on scale rows two to three, counting from the belly up. Between each line are alternating black spots over a reddish background. This characteristic helps separate this species from the plains gartersnake.

Common gartersnakes have no lip bars but have dark heads and light chins as do other gartersnakes. Their scales are strongly keeled, and they have an undivided anal plate.

Adult males are smaller but have relatively longer tails than females.

Taxonomy/Distribution and Status:

The subspecies recognized in South Dakota is the red-sided gartersnake (*T. s. parietalis*). Common gartersnakes are found east of the Rockies throughout the United States, north into the plains of Canada, and in the northwestern United States and California. This snake ranges the farthest north of any North American snake. The distribution is statewide, but they are most common in the Black Hills and in the southern and eastern parts of South Dakota. Common gartersnakes are prevalent where they are found in the state.

Habitat and Habits:

Common gartersnakes inhabit a variety of habitats. They are most commonly found in various habitats near wetlands, such as streams and ponds. In general, common gartersnakes are found in wetter habitats than the other gartersnake species found in South Dakota.

Common gartersnakes are active from April to November, depending on the weather. They are active during the day and often observed in the open. Common gartersnakes have a relatively large home range; from 22 to 35 acres in Kansas.

They mate in the early spring but may also mate in the fall near denning or overwintering sites. Males emerge first in the spring, sunning themselves near the overwintering site. Following emergence, a female may attract several males. They all attempt to mate with her, forming a "mating ball." One male inserts his hemipenes into the female's cloaca and successfully mates with her. The mated female leaves the area, while the other males await another emerging female. She gives birth to an average of 20 young in the late summer or early fall. If mated in the fall, a female can delay egg fertilization until the following spring. Females reach sexual maturity in two years. Common gartersnakes overwinter and den in

133

Common Gartersnake   Dan Fogell

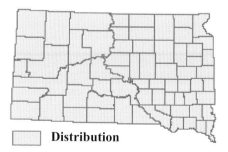

Distribution

underground sites, such as animal burrows or rock crevices.

The diet consists primarily of amphibians and earthworms but may also include insects, fish, and small mammals.

Remarks:

Common gartersnakes are also known as "garden snakes" or "grass snakes" due to their prevalence in backyards. When alarmed or threatened, they often flatten and extend their body to display the red sides. Like all gartersnakes, they release a foul-smelling musk when handled. They can also bite, and secretions from the Duvernoy's gland may sometimes cause a slight irritation at the site of the bite (see western hog-nosed snake account).

LINED SNAKE
Tropidoclonion lineatum

Description:

   Adult lined snakes measure 9 to 15 inches (22 to 38 cm) from head to tail. They are often mistaken as juvenile gartersnakes, though their belly markings are quite different. The white to yellowish belly has a double row of black markings shaped as half moons down the center. They have a gray or brown head, body, and tail. Three pale whitish or yellowish stripes run down the back, one in the center and one along each side on scale rows two and three, counting from the belly up. Lined snakes have a smaller head than gartersnakes. This species has keeled scales and an undivided anal plate. Males have relatively longer tails and smaller bodies than females.

Taxonomy/Distribution and Status:

   No subspecies is recognized in South Dakota. These snakes are abundant throughout their relatively small range, which stretches from South Dakota and Minnesota to Texas. Small populations are scattered east and west of this range. South Dakota is located in the northernmost part of the range. Lined snakes are found locally in southeastern South Dakota. Due to its rarity in South Dakota, the SDNHP monitors this species.

Habitat and Habits:

   Lined snakes are typically found in open grasslands and lightly wooded areas. They are active from April to October and more commonly observed during the fall, particularly on roads. This secretive snake is active at night, often hiding beneath stones and logs during the day. They mate in the fall, but egg fertilization is delayed until the following spring. A female gives birth to an average of six to seven young during late summer, each in its own transparent membrane. Females become sexually mature at two years of age. Lined snakes overwinter in underground sites, such as animal burrows.

   They feed primarily on earthworms.

Remarks:

   Lined snakes are relatively docile snakes. They rarely bite, but if held, they release an awful-smelling musk.

136

Lined Snake   Dan Fogell

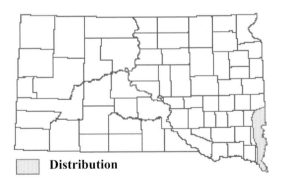

Distribution

137

Family Viperidae

The family Viperidae includes vipers and pit vipers. Vipers and pit vipers are ven-omous, and this family is considered the most advanced family of snakes due to the sophisticated venom delivery system. Large hinged, tubular fangs fit in the front of the mouth. North American vipers are pit vipers that have heat-sensing pits located between each eye and nostril. The head has numerous small scales, and the pupils are elliptical.

PRAIRIE RATTLESNAKE
Crotalus viridis
VENOMOUS

Description:

Adult prairie rattlesnakes measure 35 to 50 inches or more (90 to 127+ cm) from head to tail. The head, body, and tail are greenish gray to brown, and the belly is grayish yellow to creamy white. They have dark blotches lightly bordered in white across the back. These blotches are broad and somewhat circular toward the front but narrow and bandlike toward the rear. The tail has indistinct, dark bands. The belly has few if any markings. Prairie rattlesnakes have an undivided anal plate and keeled scales.

This snake has a rattle at the end of the tail. The triangular head has a pale stripe extending from behind each eye and reaching to each corner of the mouth. They also have vertically-elliptical pupils. This is South Dakota's only snake that is venomous to people. A heat-sensitive pit, located on each side of the head between and below the eye and nostril, helps detect prey. These pits give the pit vipers their name. They contain nerves that are sensitive to heat or warmth from warm-blooded animals. Pit vipers can detect prey in total darkness up to approx-imately one foot away. Venom is stored in venom glands. Two long, hollow fangs are folded back against the roof of the mouth until the snake is ready to strike. When the snake strikes, venom is injected from the fangs, which have moved into a striking position.

Males have longer and thicker tails than females.

Distribution and Status:

The subspecies found in South Dakota is the prairie rattlesnake (*C. v. viridis*). Prairie rattlesnakes are found in the west central United States and from Canada to Mexico. They are commonly found in counties west of and bordering the Missouri River in South Dakota. Prairie rattlesnakes were probably once common in southeastern counties of South Dakota before intensive cultivation.

Habitat and Habits:

Prairie rattlesnakes inhabit rocky bluffs and buttes, open prairies or grass-lands, and sloped talus. They are most easily seen in rocky areas, but can be found in many types of habitat, including areas along creeks and rivers. Small mammal

138

Prairie Rattlesnake   Doug Backlund

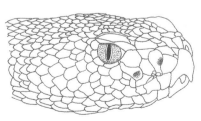

Note the elliptical pupil of the Prairie
Rattlesnake.

Rattlesnake den   Mike Erickson

burrows serve as shelter in hot or cold weather and may be used as den sites or to rear young. They also den in fissures in limestone or sandstone and can occur in large groups. They return to their den sites each year, and young snakes likely follow the scent trail of older snakes.

They are active from April to October, during the day in the spring and fall and during the night on warm days during the summer. They can be common on roads in western South Dakota in late summer, when males are searching for females.

Prairie rattlesnakes mate in the spring or fall. In northern latitudes, females produce young every other year. A female bears 8 to 17 young in August or September.

Young snakes have buttons at the tip of the tail. As they age, the buttons become the oldest rattle at the end of the tail. Young snakes shed their skin for the first time after two weeks, producing their first true rattle. Prairie rattlesnakes shed an average of twice a year, producing a new rattle after each shedding. The string of rattles often eventually breaks. A rattlesnake's age does not equal the number of rattles on the tail.

Prairie rattlesnakes prey primarily on such rodents as mice and ground squirrels.

Remarks:

Prairie rattlesnakes, while quick to flee, can be aggressive when approached. If detected, they hold their ground and rattle the tail to deter predators. Rattlesnake bites are rare, and death from a snake bite is extremely rare in the United States. Ninety-five percent of snakebite deaths in the United States are caused by western and eastern diamondback rattlesnakes.

These snakes engage in combat "dances" in which males face each other with the head and front portion of the body raised above the ground. They then smack into and twist around each other. Eventually, the stronger male throws the weaker male to the ground, apparently determining dominance.

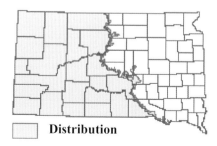

Distribution

SPECIES OF POSSIBLE NATURAL OCCURRENCE

YELLOW MUD TURTLE
Kinosternon flavescens

Description:

Yellow mud turtles measure 4 to 5 inches (10 to 13 cm) in carapace length. They have an olive-brown to olive green carapace, which is elongate and high, flat or depressed on top and keeled through the center. The carapace's sections, or scutes, may be bordered with black. The yellow mud turtle has a plain yellow or cream-colored plastron with pointed scutes and a yellow chin and throat. Other characteristics include an olive-green head and neck, upper ridges above the eyes, a short tail, and a throat with tactile whiskers. Juveniles have a rounded carapace with dark blotches on each scute. They are often yellower than adults.

Males have horny scales on the inner surface of their hind legs and horny projections on the tail, unlike females.

Taxonomy/Distribution and Status:

The subspecies recognized for this region is the yellow mud turtle (*K. f. flavescens*). This species occurs in the south central United States, particularly in the southern half of the Great Plains. They have been observed in Cherry County, Nebraska, adjacent to south central South Dakota. Habitat is available in the sandhills of south central South Dakota for these turtles, although there are no documented sightings in the state.

Habitat and Habits:

These turtles are highly aquatic and use a variety of permanent or temporary wetlands. These wetlands often have muddy bottoms and may be located in semiarid grasslands or open woodlands.

Yellow mud turtles may travel overland during rain. They burrow in mud to await more favorable weather during hot or cold temperatures.

They breed in the late spring, and females lay one to six eggs in May to June. Yellow mud turtles overwinter in burrows.

They primarily eat insects, crustaceans, mollusks, amphibians, carrion, and aquatic plants.

Yellow Mud Turtle   Dan Fogell

Plastron   Dan Fogell

REFERENCES

Anderson, D. L. 1964. A study of the relative growth of the anterior lobe of the pituitary gland in the larvae of *Rana pipiens*. M.A. Thesis. University of South Dakota, Vermillion, South Dakota. 39pp.

ASIH (American Society of Ichthyologists and Herpetologists). 2004. Guidelines for use of live amphibians and reptiles in field research home page. http://www.asih.org/pubs/ASIH_HACC_Final.PDF 15 October 2005.

Backlund, D. 2005. South Dakota statewide herpetology survey 2004. South Dakota Department of Game, Fish and Parks, unpublished report, Pierre, South Dakota. 26pp.

Ballinger, R. E., and S. M. Jones. 1985. Ecological disturbance in a sandhills prairie: Impact and importance to the lizard community on Arapaho Prairie in western Nebraska. The Prairie Naturalist 17:91-100.

Ballinger, R. E., J. W. Meeker, and M. Thies. 2000. Checklist and distribution maps of the amphibians and reptiles of South Dakota. Transactions of the Nebraska Academy of Sciences 26:29-46.

Bandas, S. J. 2003. Geographic distribution and morphometrics of South Dakota turtles. M.S. Thesis. South Dakota State University, Brookings, South Dakota. 106pp.

Baxter, G. T., and M. D. Stone. 1985. Amphibians and reptiles of Wyoming. Wyoming Game and Fish Department, Cheyenne, Wyoming. 137pp.

Breckenridge, W. J. 1943. The life history of the black-banded skink *Eumeces septentrionalis* (Baird). American Midland Naturalist 29:591-601.

Breckenridge, W. J., and J. R. Tester. 1961. Growth, local movements and hibernation of the Manitoba toad (*Bufo hemiophrys*). Ecology 42:637-646.

Brodie, H. M., and E. D. Brodie. 1982. Reptiles of North America. Golden Press, New York, New York. 240pp.

Brown, L. E., M. A. Morris, and T. R. Johnson. 1993. Zoogeography of the plains leopard frog (*Rana blairi*). Bulletin of the Chicago Academy of Sciences 15:1-12.

Bull, J. J., R. C. Vogt, and C. J. McCoy. 1982. Sex determining temperatures in turtles: A geographic comparison. Evolution 36:326-332.

Carr, M. T. 2000. Immunocytochemical localization of glutamate receptor subunits in the brain stem and cerebellum of the turtle *Chrysemys picta*. M.A. Thesis. University of South Dakota, Vermillion, South Dakota. 47pp.

Christiansen, J. L., and R. M. Bailey. 1990. The snakes of Iowa. Iowa Department of Natural Resources, Des Moines, Iowa. 16pp.

Christman, S. P. 1982. *Storeria dekayi*. Catalogue of American amphibians and reptiles. Society for the Study of Amphibians and Reptiles, New York, New York. 306.1-306.4.

Churchill, T. A., and K. B. Storey. 1992. Natural freezing survival by painted turtles *Chrysemys picta marginata* and *C. p. bellii*. American Journal of Physiology 262:R530-R537.

Collins, J. T. 1993. Amphibians and reptiles in Kansas. University Press of Kansas, Lawrence, Kansas. 397pp.

Conant, R. 1975. Field guide to reptiles and amphibians of eastern and central North America, Second Edition. Houghton Mifflin Company, Boston, Massachusetts. 429pp.

Conant, R., and J. T. Collins. 1991. Reptiles and amphibians of eastern and central North America, Third Edition. Houghton Mifflin Company, Boston, Massachusetts. 450pp.

Conant, R., and J. T. Collins. 1998. Reptiles and amphibians of eastern and central North America, Fourth Edition. Houghton Mifflin Company, New York, New York. 616pp.

Crother, B. I., J. Bundy, J. A. Campbell, K. de Queiroz, D. R. Frost, R. Highton, J. B. Iverson, P. A. Meylan, T. W. Reeder, M. E. Seidel, J. W. Sites, T. W. Taggart, S. G. Tilley, and D. B. Wake. 2000. Scientific and standard English names of amphibians and reptiles of North America north of Mexico, with comments regarding confidence in our understanding. Society for the Study of Amphibians and Reptiles, Herpetological Circular No. 29. 82pp.

Darrow, T. D. 1961. Food habits of western painted and snapping turtles in southeastern South Dakota and eastern Nebraska. M.A. Thesis. University of South Dakota, Vermillion, South Dakota. 37pp.

DeGraaf, R. M., and D. D. Rudis. 1983. Amphibians and reptiles of New England. University of Massachusetts Press, Amherst, Massachusetts. 85pp.

DelFosse, E. S. 1973. Amphibians and reptiles of South Dakota: A manual of identification and species distribution (3rd Revision). Gainesville, Florida. 34pp.

Droge, D. L., S. M. Jones, and R. E. Ballinger. 1982. Reproduction of *Holbrookia maculata* in western Nebraska. Copeia 1982:356-362.

Dunlap, D. G. 1967. Selected records of amphibians and reptiles from South Dakota. Proceedings of South Dakota Academy of Science 46:100 –106.

Edwards, J. 1999. Time course for cryoprotectant synthesis in the freeze-tolerant chorus frog (*Pseudacris triseriata*). M.A. Thesis. University of South Dakota, Vermillion, South Dakota. 25pp.

Edwards, J. R., K. L. Koster, and D. L. Swanson. 2000. Time course for cryoprotectant synthesis in the freeze-tolerant chorus frog, *Pseudacris triseriata*. Comparative Biochemistry and Physiology Part A 125:367-375.

Ernst, J. A. 2001. Assessment of the *Rana pipiens* complex in southwestern South Dakota. M.S. Thesis. University of Wisconsin, Stevens Point, Wisconsin. 50pp.

Ernst, C. H., and R. W. Barbour. 1972. Turtles of the United States. University of Kentucky Press, Lexington, Kentucky. 347pp.

Ernst, C. H., J. E. Lovich, and R. W. Barbour. 1994. Turtles of the United States and Canada. Smithsonian Institution Press, Washington, D. C. 578pp.

Ernst, C. H., and E. M. Ernst. 2003. Snakes of the United States and Canada. Smithsonian Institution Press, Washington, D. C. 668pp.

Fenwick, M. J. 1981. An analysis of spermatogenesis in *Rana pipiens*, *R. blairi*, and their hybrids. M.A. Thesis. University of South Dakota, Vermillion, South Dakota. 54pp.

Fischer, T. D. 1998. Anura of eastern South Dakota: Their distribution and characteristics of their wetland habitats, 1997-1998. M.S. Thesis. South Dakota State University, Brookings, South Dakota. 93pp.

Fischer, T. D., D. C. Backlund, K. F. Higgins, and D. E. Naugle. 1999. Field guide to South Dakota amphibians. SDAES Bulletin 733. South Dakota State University, Brookings, South Dakota. 52pp.

Fishbeck, D. W., and J. C. Underhill. 1959. A checklist of the amphibians and reptiles of South Dakota. Proceedings of South Dakota Academy of Science 38:107-113.

Fitch, H. S. 1954. Life history and ecology of the five-lined skink, *Eumeces fasciatus*. University of Kansas Publications Museum of Natural History 8:1-156.

Fitch, H. S. 1970. Reproductive cycles of lizards and snakes. University of Kansas Museum Natural History Miscellaneous Publication 52:1-247.

Fitch, H. S. 1985. Variation in clutch and litter size in New World reptiles. University of Kansas Natural History Miscellaneous Publication 76:1-76.

Flowers, M. A. 1994. Feeding ecology and habitat use of juvenile Great Plains toads (*Bufo cognatus*) and Woodhouse's toads (*B. woodhousei*). M.A. Thesis. University of South Dakota, Vermillion, South Dakota. 79pp.

Fogell, D. D. 2003. Amphibian and reptile surveys of southeastern South Dakota with emphasis on the state-endangered lined snake (*Tropidoclonian lineatum*). South Dakota Department of Game, Fish and Parks, unpublished report, Pierre, South Dakota. 22pp.

Fogell, D. D., and G. R. Cunningham. 2005. Herpetofaunal inventory of the Missouri National Recreational River and the Niobrara National Scenic River: Final Report. National Park Service, Mount Rushmore National Memorial, unpublished report, Keystone, South Dakota. 35pp.

Freeman, S., and J. C. Herron. 2004. Evolutionary Analysis (Third Edition). Pearson Education, Inc., Upple Saddle River, New Jersey. 802pp.

Frost, D. R., T. Grant, J. Faivovich, R. H. Bain, A. Hass, C. F. B. Haddad, R. O. De Sa, A. Channing, M. Wilkinson, S. C. Donnellan, C. J. Raxworthy, J. A. Campbell, B. L. Blotto, P. Moler, R. C. Drewes, R. A. Nussbaum, J. D. Lynch, D. M. Green, and W. C. Wheeler. 2006. The amphibian tree of life. Bulletin of American Museum of Natural History 297:1-370.

Gibbons, J. W., D. E. Scott, T. J. Ryan, K. A. Buhlmann, T. D. Tuberville, B. S. Metts, J. L. Greene, T. Mills, Y. Leidan, S. Poppy, and C. Winne. 2000. Reptiles in decline. BioScience 50:653-666.

Graves, B. M., and D. Duvall. 1990. Spring emergence patterns of prairie rattlesnakes and wandering garter snakes in Wyoming. Journal of Herpetology 24:351-356.

Greenwell, M., V. Beasley, and L. E. Brown. 1996. Mysterious decline of the cricket frog. Aquaticus 26:48-55.

Gronke, W. K., S. R. Chipps, S. J. Bandas, and K. F. Higgins. 2006. Reticulate melanism in western painted turtles (*Chrysemys picta bellii*): Exploring linkages with habitat and heating rates. American Midland Naturalist 156:289-298.

Hammer, D. A. 1968. Snapping turtle life history on Lacreek Refuge, South Dakota. M.S. Thesis, South Dakota State University, Brookings, South Dakota. 56pp.

Hammerson, G. A. 1982. Amphibians and reptiles in Colorado. Colorado Division of Wildlife, Denver, Colorado. 131pp.

Hardy, D. G. 1972. Some population dynamics of *Rana pipiens* in an area of southeastern South Dakota. M.A. Thesis. University of South Dakota, Vermillion, South Dakota. 49pp.

Harris, J. A. 1935. The degree of development of the bull snake embryo at time of egg laying. M.A. Thesis. University of South Dakota, Vermillion, South Dakota. 11pp.

Hay, R. 1998. Blanchard's Cricket Frogs in Wisconsin: A status report. Pages 79-82 in Lannoo, M. J., editor. Status and Conservation of Midwestern Amphibians. University of Iowa Press.

Hays, T. M., and N. J. Hays. 1999. Inventory of birds, reptiles, and amphibians on The Nature Conservancy preserves and easements in the southern Black Hills. South Dakota Department of Game, Fish and Parks, Wildlife Diversity Report 2003-04, Pierre, South Dakota. 16pp.

Heyer, W. R., M. Donnelly, R. W. McDiarmid, L. C. Hayek, and M. S. Foster. 1994. Measuring and monitoring biological diversity. Standard methods for amphibians. Smithsonian Institution Press, Washington D. C. 364pp.

Hibma, J. A., and J. C. Hibma. 2001. A preliminary amphibian and reptile survey of Rosebud Sioux Indian Reservation, Todd County, South Dakota. South Dakota Department of Game, Fish and Parks, Wildlife Diversity Report 2003-06, Pierre, South Dakota. 6pp.

Hudson, G. E. 1972. Amphibians and reptiles of Nebraska. Nebraska Conservation Bulletin 24:1-146.

Irwin, J. T., J. P. Costanzo, and R. E. Lee. 1999. Terrestrial hibernation in the northern cricket frog, *Acris crepitans*. Canadian Journal of Zoology 77:1240-1246.

Iverson, J. B., F. B. Kenneally, and A. Debevec. 1992. A revised checklist with distribution maps of turtles of the world. Green Nature Books. 400pp.

Jaslow, A. P., and R. C. Vogt. 1977. Identification and distribution of *Hyla versicolor* and *Hyla chrysoscelis* in Wisconsin. Herpetologica 33:201-205.

Jenkins, J. L. 2000. Bioenergetics of freeze-thaw cycles in the chorus frog (*Pseudacris triseriata*). M.A. Thesis. University of South Dakota,

Vermillion, South Dakota. 42pp.

Jessen, T. 2002. Field notes for the eastern South Dakota reptile and amphibian survey. South Dakota Department of Game, Fish and Parks, unpublished report, Pierre, South Dakota. 10pp.

Jessen, T. 2003. A survey of herpetofauna of the Big Sioux River valley. South Dakota Department of Game, Fish and Parks, unpublished report, Pierre, South Dakota. 15pp.

Johnson, T. R. 1987. Amphibians and reptiles of Missouri. Missouri Department of Conservation, Jefferson City, Missouri. 368pp.

Johnson, T. R. 2000. Amphibians and reptiles of Missouri. Second Edition. Missouri Department of Conservation, Jefferson City, Missouri. 400pp.

Johnson, V. O. 1935. Anatomy of the digestive and urogenital systems of the horned toad. M.A. Thesis. University of South Dakota, Vermillion, South Dakota. 19pp.

Jung, R. E. 1993. Blanchard's cricket frogs in southwest Wisconsin. Transactions of Wisconsin Academy of Science, Arts and Letters 81:81-89.

Karns, D. R. 1986. Field herpetology: Methods for the study of reptiles and amphibians in Minnesota. James Ford Bell Museum of Natural History University of Minnesota Occasional Paper 18:1- 88.

Kirsch, S. 1983. Ecology of the eastern hognose snake in southeastern South Dakota. M.A. Thesis. University of South Dakota, Vermillion, South Dakota. 42pp.

Kitchell, J., and B. Hay. 2004. Frog and toad survey: 2004. Wisconsin Department of Natural Resources Annual Report, Madison, Wisconsin. 8pp.

Klauber, L. M. 1972. Rattlesnakes: Their habits, life histories and influence on mankind. University of California Press, Berkeley, California. 1533pp.

Kruse, K. C. 1973. Two morphotypes of the *Rana pipiens* complex in the central plains states. M.A. Thesis. University of South Dakota, Vermillion, South Dakota. 34pp.

Layne, J. R., Jr., and A. L. Jones. 2001. Freeze tolerance in the gray treefrog: Cryoprotectant mobilization and organ dehydration. Journal of Experimental Zoology 290:1-5.

McCallum, M. L., and S. E. Trauth. 2006. An evaluation of the subspecies *Acris crepitans blanchardi* (Anura, Hylidae). Zootaxa 1104:1–21.

NatureServe. 2006. NatureServe: A network connecting science with conservation. NatureServe homepage. http://www.natureserve.org 17 October 2006.

NBII (National Biological Information Infrastructure). 2006. FrogWeb: Amphibian declines and malformations webpage. http://frogweb.nbii.gov/ 1 Aug 2006.

Nelson, D. E. 1965. Histology of the thyroid and neurohypophysis in leopard frog larvae grown under crowded conditions. M.A. Thesis. University of South Dakota, Vermillion, South Dakota. 38pp.

Newman, L. C., S. S. Sands, D. R. Wallace, and C. W. Stevens. 2002. Characterization of mu, kappa, and delta opioid binding in amphibian whole brain tissue homogenates. Journal of Pharmacology and Experimental Therapeutics 301:364-370.

Niebel, D. B. 1979. The effect of work load on taurine synthesis in frog heart. M.A. Thesis. University of South Dakota, Vermillion, South Dakota. 57pp.

Oldham, J. C., and H. M. Smith. 1991. The generic status of the smooth green snake *Opheodrys vernalis*. Bulletin of the Maryland Herpetological Society 27:201-215.

Oldfield, B., and J. J. Moriarty. 1994. Amphibians and reptiles native to Minnesota. University of Minnesota Press, Minneapolis, Minnesota. 237pp.

Olson, R. D. 2001. Calling survey for the Blanchard's cricket frog (*Acris crepitans blanchardi*) in Tripp County, South Dakota. South Dakota Department of Game, Fish and Parks, Wildlife Diversity Report 2003-07, Pierre, South Dakota. 4pp.

Over, W. 1923. Amphibians and reptiles of South Dakota. South Dakota Geological and Natural History Survey Series XXIII Bulletin No. 10. University of South Dakota, Vermillion, South Dakota. 43pp.

Over, W. 1943. Amphibians and reptiles of South Dakota. Natural History Studies No. VI. University of South Dakota, Vermillion, South Dakota. 31pp.

Packard, G. C., and M. J. Packard. 2001. The overwintering strategy of hatchling painted turtles, or how to survive in the cold without freezing. BioScience 51:199-207.

Pappas, M. J., B. J. Brecke, and J. D. Congdon. 2000. Blanding's turtles of Weaver Dunes, Minnesota. Chelonian Conservation and Biology 3:557-568.

Patton, F. A. 1926. Our trip to the Eagle's nest. The Oologist 43:30.

Perkins, K., and D. Backlund. 2000. Freshwater mussels of the Missouri River National Recreational River below Gavins Point Dam, South Dakota and Nebraska. South Dakota Department of Game, Fish and Parks, Wildlife Division Report 2000-01, Pierre, South Dakota. 23pp.

Peterson, C. R. 1974. Preliminary report on the amphibians and reptiles of the Black Hills of South Dakota and Wyoming. Unpublished M.S. Thesis, University of Illinois, Urbana-Champaign, Illinois. 59pp.

Platz, J. E. 1989. Speciation within the chorus frog (*Pseudacris triseriata*): Morphometric and mating call analyses of the boreal and western subspecies. Copeia 1989:704-712.

Plummer, M. V., and H. W. Shirer. 1975. Movement patterns in a river population of the softshell turtle, *Trionyx muticus*. Occasional Papers, University of Kansas Museum of Natural History 43:1-26.

Plummer, M. V., and N. E. Mills. 1996. Observations on trailing and mating behaviors in hognose snakes (*Heterodon platirhinos*). Journal of Herpetology 30:80-82.

Pough, F. H., R. M. Andrews, J. E. Cadle, M. L. Crump, A. H. Savitzky, and K. D. Wells. 2004. Herpetology. Third Edition. Prentice Hall, Upple Saddle River, New Jersey. 726pp.

Preston, W. B. 1982. Amphibians and reptiles of Manitoba. Manitoba Museum of Man and Nature, Winnipeg, Canada. 128pp.

Reeder, T. W., C. J. Cole, and H.C. Dessauer. 2002. Phylogenetic relationships of whiptail lizards of the genus *Cnemidophorus* (Squamata: Teiidae): A test of monophyly, reevaluation of karyotypic evolution, and review of hybrid origins. American Museum Novitates 3365:1-61.

Ritke, M. E., J. G. Babb, and M. K. Ritke. 1990. Life history of the gray treefrog (*Hyla chrysoscelis*) in western Tennessee. Journal of Herpetology 24:135-141.

Rossman, D. A., N. B. Ford, and R. A. Seigel. 1996. The garter snakes: Evolution and ecology. University of Oklahoma Press, Norman, Oklahoma. 332pp.

Schmid, W. D. 1982. Survival of frogs in low temperature. Science 215:697-698.

Schramm, M. A. 1977. Taurine synthesis in dog and frog heart. PhD Dissertation. University of South Dakota, Vermillion, South Dakota. 90pp.

SDNHP (South Dakota Natural Heritage Program). 2006. Rare, threatened, or endangered animals tracked by the Natural Heritage Program homepage. http://www.state.sd.us/gfp/DivisionWildlife/Diversity/RareAnimal.htm.

Sherbrooke, W. C. 2003. Introduction to horned lizards of North America. California Natural History Guides No. 64. University of California Press, Berkeley, California. 191pp.

Smith, H. M. 1963. The identity of the Black Hills population of *Storeria occipotomaculata,* the red-bellied snake. Herpetologica 19:16-21.

Smith, H. M. 1971. Handbook of lizards. Comstock Publishing Associates, Ithaca, New York. 557pp.

Smith, P. W. 1961. Amphibians and reptiles of Illinois. Bulletin of Illinois Natural History Survey 28:1-298.

Smith, H. M., R. Mixter, and T. Spangler. 1966. The bullfrog and other reptiles and amphibians in western South Dakota. Journal of the Ohio Herpetological Society 5:106-107.

Smith, H. M., and E. D. Brodie, Jr. 1982. Reptiles of North America: A guide to field identification. Golden Press, New York. 240pp.

Smith, B. E., L. R. Cottingham, C. R. Peterson, and M. J. Goode. 2004. A herpetofaunal report of the Black Hills, summer 2004. South Dakota Department of Game, Fish and Parks, unpublished report, Pierre, South Dakota. 46pp.

Stafford, P. 2000. Snakes. Smithsonian Institute Press, Washington, D. C. 112pp.

Stebbins, R. C. 1985. A field guide to western reptiles and amphibians. Second Edition. Houghton Mifflin Company, Boston, Massachusetts. 336pp.

Stebbins, R. C. 2003. A field guide to western reptiles and amphibians. Third Edition. Houghton Mifflin Company, Boston, Massachusetts. 533pp.

Storey, K. B. 1987. Glycolysis and the regulation of cryoprotectant synthesis in liver of the freeze tolerant wood frog. Journal of Comparative Physiology B175:373-380.

Storey, K. B., J. M. Storey, S. P. J. Brooks, T. A. Churchill, and R. J. Brooks. 1988. Hatchling turtles survive freezing during winter hibernation. Proceedings of Natural Academy of Sciences USA 85:8350-8354.

Swanson, D. L., and B. M. Graves. 1995. Supercooling and freeze intolerance in overwintering juvenile spadefoot toads (*Scaphiopus bombifrons*). Journal of Herpetology 29:280-285.

Swanson, D. L., B. M. Graves, and K. L. Koster. 1996. Freezing tolerance/intolerance and cryoprotectant synthesis in terrestrially overwintering anurans in the Great Plains, USA. Journal of Comparative Physiology, B: Biochemical, Systematic, and Environmental Physiology 166:110-119.

Theroux, S. 2002. Animal Kingdom: Classification of Reptiles Homepage. http://www.swishweb.com/Animal_Kingdom/animal03.htm 28 March 2003.

Thompson, S. 1976. Herps from each county. South Dakota Department of Game, Fish and Parks, unpublished report, Pierre, South Dakota.

Thompson, S., and D. Backlund. 1999. South Dakota snakes: A guide to snake identification. South Dakota Department of Game, Fish and Parks, Pierre, South Dakota. 28pp.

Timken, R. L. 1968. The distribution and ecology of turtles in South Dakota. PhD Dissertation. University of South Dakota, Vermillion, South Dakota. 110pp.

Timken, R. L. 1969. Ornate box turtle distribution in South Dakota. Herpetologica 25:70.

Trapido, H. 1944. The snakes of the genus *Storeria*. American Midland Naturalist 31:1-84.

Vitt, L. J., and W. E. Cooper, Jr. 1986. Skink reproduction and sexual dimorphism: *Eumeces fasciatus* in the southeastern United States, with notes on *Eumeces inexpectatus*. Journal of Herpetology 20:65-76.

Vogt, R. C. 1981. Natural history of amphibians and reptiles in Wisconsin. Milwaukee Public Museum, Milwaukee, Wisconsin. 205pp.

Warner, D. A., and R. M. Andrews. 2002. Nest-site selection in relation to temperature and moisture by the lizard *Sceloporus undulatus*. Herpetologica 58:399-407.

Werner, J. K., B. A. Maxell, P. Hendricks, and D. L. Flath. 2004. Amphibians and reptiles of Montana. Mountain Press Publishing Company, Missoula, Montana. 262 pp.

Wilmot, R., M. Baker, T. Horton, and K. Meerdink. 2001. Cricket frog survey: Union County, South Dakota. South Dakota Department of Game, Fish and Parks, Wildlife Diversity Report 2003-07, Pierre, South Dakota. 42pp.

Woodbury, A. M. 1931. Descriptive catalog of reptiles of Utah. Bulletin of University of Utah 21:1-129.

Zamudio, K. R., K. B. Jones, and R. H. Ward. 1997. Molecular systematics of short-horned lizards: Biogeography and taxonomy of a widespread species complex. Systematic Biology 46:284-305.

GLOSSARY

Amplexus clasping behavior of amphibians during breeding.

Anal plate a scale that surrounds the cloacal opening at the lower end of the digestive tract in reptiles.

Aquatic describes animals that live in water.

Arboreal describes animals that are found in or upon woods or trees.

Arthropod invertebrate animals, such as insects, arachnids, and crustaceans, that have a jointed body and limbs and usually have a chitinous shell that is molted.

Bask to rest in sunlight in order to absorb the sun's energy and warmth.

Bioindicator an organism and/or biological process where a change in numbers, structure, or function points to changes in the integrity or quality of the environment.

Boss a raised, rounded area between the eyes or on the snout of some toad species.

Button first rattle segment on a young rattlesnake.

Carapace the upper (dorsal) shell of a turtle.

Carnivorous describes an animal that primarily eats meat.

Chytridiomycosis an infectious disease caused by the chytrid fungus, often affecting amphibians.

Cloaca the common chamber into which intestinal, urinary, and reproductive tracts empty and which opens to the exterior through the anus.

Cloacal lips margin of flesh around the cloaca.

Clutch complete set of eggs incubated or produced at one time.

Concave curving inward.

Copulate to engage in sexual intercourse.

Coulee a deep gulch or ravine with sloping sides; often dry in the summer.

Cranial crest/ridge a raised ridge between or behind the eyes of some toad species.

Cryoprotectant a substance that is used to protect biological tissue from freezing damage.

Dichotomous key a guide to identification of plants or animals consisting of a series of pairs of questions or descriptions.

Disturbance any event or series of events that disrupts ecosystem, community, or population structure and alters the physical environment.

Diurnal active in daylight.

Dorsal refers to the back or top of an animal.

Dorsolateral fold fold or ridge of skin that runs from behind the head down the length of the back.

Dorsum the entire upper surface of an animal.

Ecosystem a system formed by the interaction of a community of organisms with their physical environment.

Ectotherm an animal whose body temperature is largely dependent upon its environment; cold-blooded.

Endangered species a species that is facing extinction.

Endemic a species that is unique to a place or region, found naturally nowhere else.

Endotherm an animal that has internal mechanisms for maintaining body temperature; warm-blooded.

Estivation when an animal is in a state of seclusion and inactivity during periods of drought or high temperatures.

External fertilization a method of reproduction most common in aquatic organisms during which the egg and sperm unite outside the body.

Extirpated a species that has been eliminated from a particular area, but still exists somewhere else.

Food chain transfer of food energy from plants to one or more animals; a sequence of organisms in which each is food for the next organism in the sequence.

Gelatinous rubbery, slimy, or jellylike substance in which eggs may be embedded.

Gravid pregnant.

Habitat the surroundings or locality where a plant or an animal is ordinarily found.

Habitat degradation the negative impact on habitat and ecosystem size or quality resulting from human disturbances or land use changes commonly associated with urban or agricultural development.

Hemipenis one of the pair of reproductive organs in male snakes and lizards that are held inverted in the body but are everted for reproduction through an erectile tissue.

Herbivorous describes an animal that eats plants.

Herpetofauna reptiles and amphibians.

Herpetologists biologists who study reptiles and amphibians.

Hibernation when an animal is in an inactive or dormant state for a period, usually winter.

Home range the area within which an animal tends to confine all or nearly all of its activities for a long period of time.

Hybridize to crossbreed between parents of different races or varieties.

Internal fertilization a form of animal sexual reproduction in which a sperm cell is united with an egg cell within the body of the female of the species.

Invasive species a species whose introduction does or is likely to cause economic or environmental harm or harm to human health.

Jacobson's organ sensory organ found in the roof of the mouth of many terrestrial amphibians, reptiles, and mammals. Snakes use this organ in combination with their forked tongue to sense odors.

Keel a narrow ridge running down the back of some turtle and snake species; also refers to the ridge on individual scales of some snakes and lizards.

Labial scale one of a group of scales along the upper side of the mouth of reptiles.

Lateral refers to the sides of an animal.

Life cycle the series of changes occurring in the life of an organism.

Medial refers to the middle of an animal.

Metamorphosis a change in form or structure, especially the significant physical transformation undergone by various animals during development, such as a tadpole to a frog.

Migration movement of an animal from one region to another, usually occurring with the change in seasons.

Mima mounds pocket gopher mounds covered with "weedy" vegetation.

Neoteny the state resulting when juvenile characteristics are retained by the adults of a species; also known as paedomorphism.

Neurohypophysis posterior portion of the pituitary gland.

Niche the unique environment or set of ecological conditions in which a specific plant or animal species occurs and the function the organism serves within that ecosystem.

Nocturnal describes animals that are active at night.

Nonvenomous refers to an animal that does not produce toxic venom.

Ocelli an eye spot.

Opioid agonist a drug or medication that can both activate and block opioid receptors.

Oviparous method of reproduction in which fertilized eggs are laid by the female and develop outside her body.

Ovoviviparous method of reproduction in which fertilized eggs develop within the female but the embryo receives no nutritional materials from the female.

Parotid gland prominent glands on the shoulder, neck, or back of the eyes of toads that produce toxic secretions.

Plasma glycerol a natural antifreeze produced by the liver.

Plastron the lower (ventral) shell of a turtle.

Quadrate bone a jaw bone in all vertebrates, except mammals, that articulates with the lower jaw bone; in snakes it is elongated and mobile, allowing large prey items to be swallowed; in mammals, this bone has evolved into the incus, one of the small bones of the inner ear.

Riffle a reach of stream characterized by shallow, fast-moving water broken by the presence of rocks and boulders.

Scute an external bony or horny plate; one of the enlarged scales covering the exterior of a turtle shell.

Seining a method of catching fish using seine nets that typically results in significant bycatch.

Semifossorial somewhat adapted for digging.

Semipermeable describes a membrane that will allow some but not all substances to pass through it.

Sexual dimorphism a distinct difference in appearance between males and females of the same species.

South Dakota Natural Heritage Program/Database (SDNHP/SDNHD) source for information on South Dakota's native species and habitats, emphasizing those of conservation concern; program staff collect and distribute information to assist in natural resource conservation and management; part of an international network of information sources on rare species and unique habitats.

Species a group of organisms all of which have a high degree of physical and genetic similarity and generally interbreed only among themselves.

Spermatophore a capsule or mass containing sperm formed in males of some species.

Spectacle a thin, transparent scale over a snake's eye that is shed with its skin.

Spermatogenesis formation and development of spermatozoa.

Subspecies a segment of a certain species, usually due to their natural separation; different from other populations of the same species but still able to interbreed with them.

Tactile perceptible to the sense of touch; used for feeling.

Tadpoles aquatic larvae of frogs and toads.

Taurine a colorless crystalline substance obtained from the bile of mammals.

Terrestrial describes animals that live on land.

Territory a particular area defended by an animal against intrusion by other animals, particularly those of the same species.

Threatened species describes a species of animal that is not endangered but may become so in the future.

Tibia the leg of toads and frogs from heel to knee.

Tubercle a raised projection or bump on the skin.

Tympanum rounded eardrum on the side of the head of frogs and toads.

Venomous describes an animal capable of delivering a toxic venom against prey and/or natural enemies through a sting or bite.

Vent the external opening of the cloaca in reptiles.

Venter the entire lower surface or belly of an animal.

Ventral refers to the bottom or underside of an animal.

Appendix A. Museum Specimen Records

Museum specimens collected from various museums throughout the country (Ballinger et al. 2000). Included are the total number of amphibian and reptile specimens by museum (Ballinger pers. comm.).

Museum	Total Specimens
Academy of National Sciences	39
American Museum of Natural History	110
California Academy of Science	18
Carnegie Museum of Natural History	48
Field Museum of Natural History (Chicago)	95
Florida Museum of Natural History	3
Illinois Natural History Survey	35
Iowa State University	10
Los Angeles County Museum of Natural History	7
Louisiana Museum of Natural History (Louisiana State University)	12
Milwaukee Public Museum	2
Museum of Comparative Zoology (Harvard University)	53
Museum of Vertebrate Zoology (University of California, Berkeley)	54
Oklahoma Museum of Natural History	8
San Diego Museum of Natural History	1,201
Sternberg Museum of Natural History (Fort Hays State University)	2
Texas A & M University	14
United States National Museum	312
University of Colorado Museum	50
University of Illinois Museum of Natural History	83
University of Kansas Museum of Natural History	560
University of Michigan Museum of Zoology	203
University of Nebraska State Museum	2
University of Nebraska, Kearney	1
University of South Dakota*	4,549

*now curated at the University of Nebraska State Museum

Appendix B. Checklist of Amphibians and Reptiles of South Dakota

AMPHIBIANS (15 species)

Order Caudata (Salamanders)
_____ Tiger Salamander   *Ambystoma tigrinum*
_____ Mudpuppy   *Necturus maculosus*

Order Anura (Frogs and Toads)
_____ American Toad   *Anaxyrus americanus*
_____ Great Plains Toad   *Anarxyrus cognatus*
_____ Canadian Toad   *Anaxyrus hemiophrys*
_____ Woodhouse's Toad   *Anaxyrus woodhousii*
_____ Northern Cricket Frog   *Acris crepitans*
_____ Cope's Gray Treefrog   *Hyla chrysoscelis*
_____ Gray Treefrog   *Hyla versicolor*
_____ Boreal Chorus Frog   *Pseudacris maculata*
_____ Plains Spadefoot   *Spea bombifrons*
_____ Plains Leopard Frog   *Lithobates blairi*
_____ Bullfrog   *Lithobates catesbeiana*
_____ Northern Leopard Frog   *Lithobates pipiens*
_____ Wood Frog   *Lithobates sylvaticus*

REPTILES (31 species)

Order Testudines (Turtles)
_____ Snapping Turtle   *Chelydra serpentina*
_____ Painted Turtle   *Chrysemys picta*
_____ Blanding's Turtle   *Emys blandingii*
_____ False Map Turtle   *Graptemys pseudogeographica*
_____ Western Box Turtle   *Terrapene ornata*
_____ Smooth Softshell   *Apalone mutica*
_____ Spiny Softshell   *Apalone spinifera*

Order Squamata (Lizards and Snakes)
_____ Lesser Earless Lizard   *Holbrookia maculata*
_____ Sagebrush Lizard   *Sceloporus graciosus*
_____ Prairie Lizard   *Sceloporus undulatus*
_____ Short-horned Lizard   *Phrynosoma hernandesi*
_____ Five-lined Skink   *Eumeces fasciatus*
_____ Many-lined Skink   *Eumeces multivirgatus*
_____ Prairie Skink   *Eumeces septentrionalis*
_____ Six-lined Racerunner   *Aspidoscelis sexlineata*

___	Racer	*Coluber constrictor*
___	Ring-necked Snake	*Diadophis punctatus*
___	Western Foxsnake	*Elaphe vulpina*
___	Western Hog-nosed Snake	*Heterodon nasicus*
___	Eastern Hog-nosed Snake	*Heterodon platirhinos*
___	Milksnake	*Lampropeltis triangulum*
___	Northern Watersnake	*Nerodia sipedon*
___	Smooth Green Snake	*Liochlorophis vernalis*
___	Gophersnake (Bullsnake)	*Pituophis catenifer*
___	Brownsnake	*Storeria dekayi*
___	Redbelly Snake	*Storeria occipitomaculata*
___	Terrestrial Gartersnake	*Thamnophis elegans*
___	Plains Gartersnake	*Thamnophis radix*
___	Common Gartersnake	*Thamnophis sirtalis*
___	Lined Snake	*Tropidoclonion lineatum*
___	Prairie Rattlesnake	*Crotalus viridis*

Appendix C. Key to Amphibians and Reptiles of South Dakota

Dichotomous keys are helpful tools when attempting to identify herpeto-fauna. Identifying certain species may be difficult. In these cases photographs can help a herpetologist in a wildlife agency or university identify the species. Because some species are rare or thought to be absent in South Dakota, definitive identifications can help to further document the herpetofauna of the state.

To use dichotomous keys, read the couplet descriptions (choices A or B) at each number starting with one, and choose the best alternative (choice A or B) at each number. This process will lead you through the key until the identity of the herp is revealed. Note that a key may not work for every specimen because some individuals vary in size, color, and other characteristics from the norm. Look at the known distribution in South Dakota of the herp in question. In certain cases in the text, we have pointed out species that may be difficult to identify. Except for the salamanders, characteristics in these keys apply only to adult animals.

Amphibian keys are reproduced by permission from the Agricultural Experiment Station at South Dakota State University. Amphibian keys were orig-inally included in Fischer et al. (1999). The snake key is reproduced by permis-sion from South Dakota Department of Game, Fish and Parks and was originally included in Thompson and Backlund (1999).

Abbreviations used in keys:

TL= total length; the distance from the tip of the snout to the end of the tail
TaL = tail length; the distance from the posterior edge of the vent to the end of the tail
SVL = snout to vent length; the distance from the tip of the snout to the posterior edge of the vent
CL = carapace length; the straight line measurement between the anterior and posterior ends of the carapace

Source of abbreviations and labeling styles: *Amphibians and Reptiles of Montana* (Werner et al. 2004)

Amphibian Keys

1A   Animal has a tail   **Go to Key 1 (Salamanders)**
1B   Animal does not have a tail   **Go to Key 2 (Frogs and Toads)**

Key 1   Salamanders
Amphibians with tails

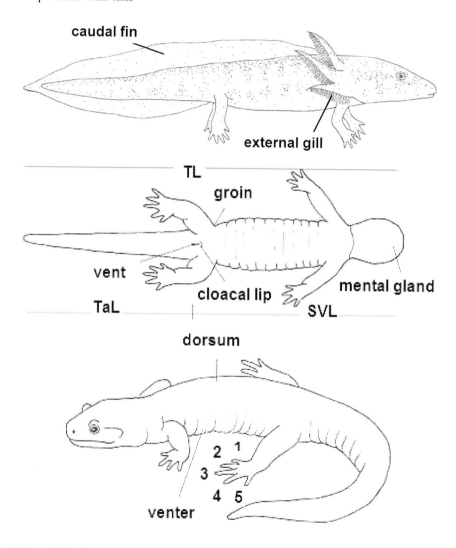

1A   Gills absent   **Tiger Salamander (p. 16)**
1B   Gills present   **Go to 2**

2A   Gills feathery, not red; 5 toes on hind foot
                            Larval Tiger Salamander (p. 16)

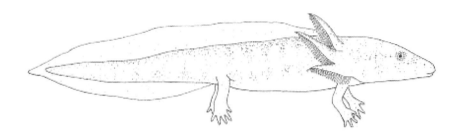

2B   Gills clumped and red; 4 toes on hind foot
                            Mudpuppy (p. 19)

Key 2   Frogs and Toads
Amphibians without tails

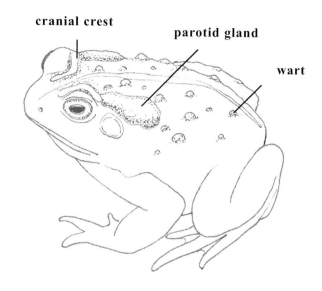

cranial crest

parotid gland

wart

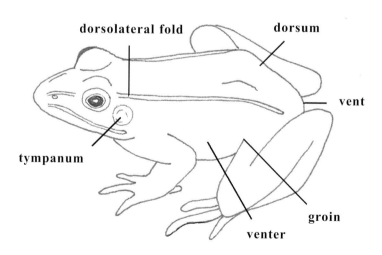

dorsolateral fold

dorsum

vent

tympanum

groin

venter

1A	Skin dry and warty	**Go to 2**
1B	Skin smooth and moist	**Go to 5**
2A	Warts small and uniform	**Great Plains Toad (p. 24)**
2B	Warts vary in size and clumped	**Go to 3**

3A	Underside is completely white	**Woodhouse's Toad (p. 28)**
3B	Underside with heavy black/gray flecking	
		Go to 4

4A	Cranial ridges separate	**American Toad (p. 21)**

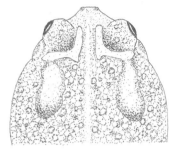

4B	Cranial ridges form single raised bump between eyes (boss)	
		Canadian Toad (p. 26)

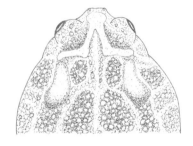

5A	Suction cups on toes; can stick to vertical surface	
		Go to 6

5B	No suction cups on toes	**Go to 9**

| 6A | Suction cups as wide as toes | **Go to 7** |
| 6B | Suction cups wider than toes | **Go to 8** |

7A	Striped pattern on back	**Boreal Chorus Frog (p. 40)**
7B	Dark green or brown triangle on head	
		Northern Cricket Frog (p. 31)

8A	Dark borders present around dark spots	
		Gray Treefrog (p. 37)
8B	Dark borders absent around dark spots	
		Cope's Gray Treefrog (p. 34)

| 9A | Dorsolateral folds absent | **Go to 10** |
| 9B | Dorsolateral folds present | **Go to 11** |

10A	Extensive webbing on hind feet, green body color	
		Bullfrog (p. 49)
10B	Hard, dark colored "spade" on hind feet	
		Plains Spadefoot (p. 43)

| 11A | Spots on body and legs | **Go to 12** |
| 11B | Body uniform brownish color | **Wood Frog (p. 55)** |

| 12A | Dorsolateral folds complete and unbroken (left drawing below) | |
| | | **Northern Leopard Frog (p. 52)** |

12B Dorsolateral folds interrupted and broken toward the rear of the animal (right drawing below) **Plains Leopard Frog (p. 46)**

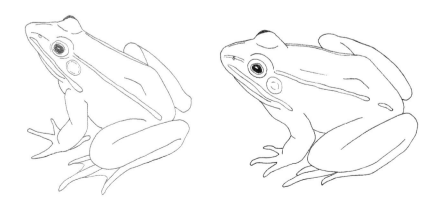

Reptile Keys

1A   Hard or soft outer shell with a carapace and plastron present
                                      Go to Key 1 (Turtles)
1B   Hard or soft outer shell with a carapace and plastron absent
                                      Go to 2

2A   Legs are present   **Go to Key 2 (Lizards)**
2B   Legs are absent   **Go to Key 3 (Snakes)**

Key 1   Turtles
Reptiles with hard or soft outer shell with carapace and plastron

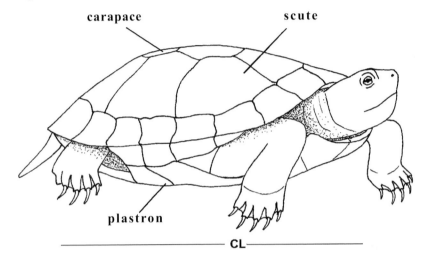

PLASTRON

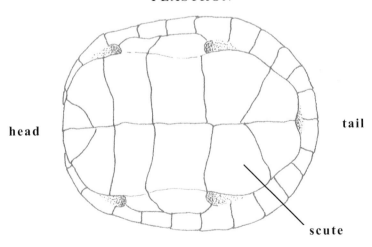

1A	Soft outer shell	**Go to 2**
1B	Hard outer shell	**Go to 3**

2A   Outer shell with numerous small spines (feels like sandpaper); nasal septum present   **Spiny Softshell (p. 79)**

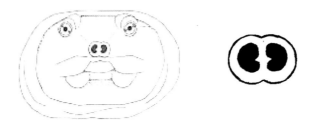

2B   Outer shell without numerous small spines; nasal septum not present

                                   Smooth Softshell (p. 76)

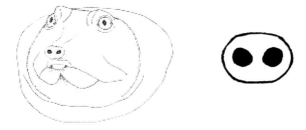

3A   Plastron "X" shaped; plastron incompletely covering belly

                                   Snapping Turtle (p. 60)

3B   Plastron not "X" shaped; plastron completely covering belly

                                   Go to 4

4A   Carapace dome shaped; no distinct yellow lines on head, appendages and tail   **Go to 5**

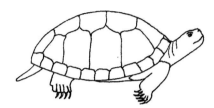

4B   Carapace not dome shaped; distinct yellow lines on head, appendages and tail   **Go to 6**

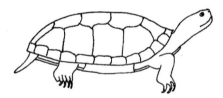

5A   Bright yellow chin; hinged plastron yellow with some black speckling
                                          Blanding's Turtle (p. 67)

5B   No bright yellow chin; hinged plastron dark with radiating yellow lines on scutes   **Western Box Turtle (p. 73)**

6A   "L" shaped yellow lines on head; plastron yellow with black outlining on scutes   **False Map Turtle (p. 70)**

6B   Yellow lines on head not "L" shaped but irregular; plastron dark with red blotches   **Painted Turtle (p. 63)**

Key 2   Lizards
Reptiles with four legs, a tail, and no shell

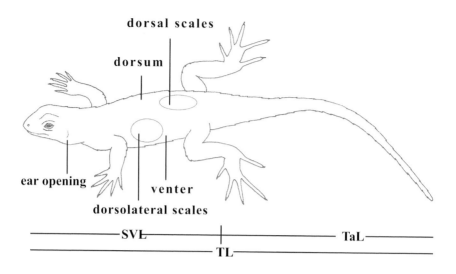

1A   Scales smooth appearing shiny   **Go to 2**
1B   Scales rough appearing dull   **Go to 4**

2A   Dark and light lines alternate across dorsum; light dorsolateral lines
     on fourth and fifth row of scales do not extend onto the head
                                        Prairie Skink (p. 95)
2B   Dark and light lines alternate across dorsum; light dorsolateral lines
     not restricted to fourth and fifth row of scales
                                        Go to 3

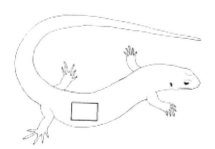

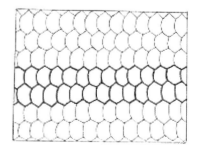

3A Prominent light stripe restricted to third scale row (from midline of back) **Many-lined Skink (p. 93)**
3B Five light stripes dorsally forming a "Y" on head **Five-lined Skink (p. 91)**

4A Horns cover dorsum, sides, and appendages; body flattened; head and legs short **Short-horned Lizard (p. 89)**
4B Horns do not cover dorsum, sides, and appendages; body not flattened **Go to 5**

5A No external ear openings present, short black bars behind armpits **Lesser Earless Lizard (p. 82)**

5B External ear openings present, faint dorsal stripes along back **Go to 6**

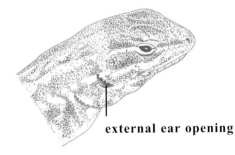

external ear opening

6A Sharply keeled, spiny dorsal scales present **Go to 7**
6B Smooth dorsal scales; body color greenish; long tail **Six-lined Racerunner (p. 97)**

7A Granular, nonoverlapping scales on posterior surface of thigh; two distinct light-colored lateral stripes **Prairie Lizard (p. 87)**
7B Keeled, overlapping scales on posterior surface of thigh; no distinct light-colored lateral stripes **Sagebrush Lizard (p. 85)**

Key 3   Snakes
Legs are absent

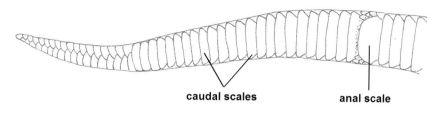

caudal scales   **anal scale**

preocular scale   **postocular scale**

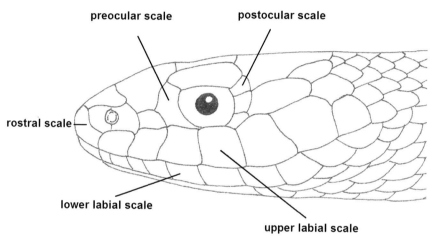

rostral scale

lower labial scale

upper labial scale

1A   Rattle segments at the end of tail   **Prairie Rattlesnake (p. 138)**

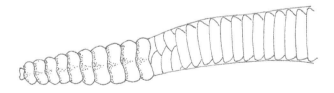

1B   No rattle segments at the end of tail

Go to 2

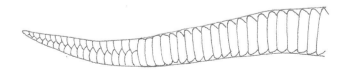

2A Scales keeled   **Go to 3**

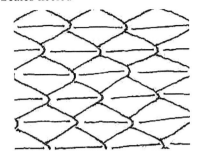

2B Scales not keeled or only weakly keeled on top and not keeled on
    sides   **Go to 12**

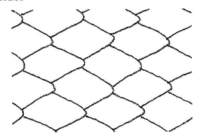

3A Snout upturned and shovellike   **Go to 4**

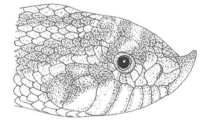

3B Snout not upturned and shovellike

                                        Go to 5

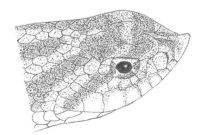

| 4A | Belly and underside of tail black or checkered black and white, snout sharply upturned | **W. Hog-nosed Snake (p. 108)** |
| 4B | Belly blackish but underside of tail light-colored (not black), snout only slightly upturned | **E. Hog-nosed Snake (p. 111)** |

| 5A | Belly uniform color of red, tan, pinkish, or orangish | **Go to 6** |
| 5B | Belly not of uniform color of red, tan, pinkish, or orangish | **Go to 7** |

| 6A | Belly uniform color of red or orange | **Redbelly Snake (p. 125)** |
| 6B | Belly uniform color of pink or tan | **Brownsnake (p. 123)** |

| 7A | Three or more longitudinal stripes along length of body | **Go to 8** |
| 7B | No longitudinal stripes on body | **Go to 11** |

| 8A | Longitudinal stripes pale, double row of black half moons on the white or yellowish belly, found only in southeastern South Dakota | **Lined Snake (p. 136)** |
| 8B | Longitudinal stripes bright yellow, orange, or red | **Go to 9** |

| 9A | Vertical black bars on the scales of lips (labial scales) | **Plains Gartersnake (p. 130)** |
| 9B | No vertical black bars on the scales of lips | **Go to 10** |

| 10A | Reddish stripe or bars on each side of body | **Common Gartersnake (p. 133)** |
| 10B | No reddish stripe or bars on each side of body, color duller than other gartersnakes; found only in Black Hills | **Terrestrial Gartersnake (p. 128)** |

11A Body color tan to reddish brown to gray with darker bands or blotches along the body; mostly aquatic; found only along Missouri River in Bon Homme County   **Northern Watersnake (p. 117)**

11B Yellowish body color with brown or black blotches; resembles western foxsnake but gophersnake has all scales keeled, more pointed nose, undivided anal plate, and strong head markings
   Gophersnake (p. 121)

undivided anal plate

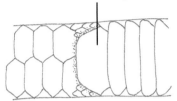

12A Body color of red or orange bands bordered with black, separated by yellow or white bands   **Go to 13**

12B Body color not of red or orange, black, and yellow or white bands
   Go to 14

13A Top of head red, with a white or yellowish collar
   Red Milksnake (p. 114)

13B Top of head black or orange (applies to both subspecies of milksnake; intergrades occur in South Dakota, making some individuals difficult to identify)
   Pale Milksnake (p. 114)

14A Body color yellowish to light brown with bold brown to black blotches, divided anal plate, and almost no marking on head (resembles gophersnake but scales on foxsnake are only weakly keeled on top and not keeled on sides. The foxsnake also has a broad, rounded nose, few or no markings on head, and a divided anal plate)

Western Foxsnake (p. 106)

divided anal plate

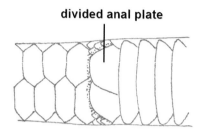

14B No bold brown to black blotches, body color nearly uniform, may have ring around neck   **Go to 15**

15A Bright yellow or orange-yellow ring around neck

Ring-necked Snake (p. 103)

15B No yellow ring around neck   **Go to 16**

16A Body color bright green (bright green color fades to a pale blue after death and may be confused with adult racer but smooth green snakes rarely exceed 20 inches in length)

Smooth Green Snake (p. 119)

16B Body color green to blue, but not bright green (juvenile racers have dark blotches along back, spotted sides, and scattered dark speckles on belly, much like milksnake or gophersnake, but racers have divided anal plates while milksnake and gophersnake have single anal plates)   **Racer (p. 100)**

Appendix D. Chorus Chronology of Breeding Anurans*

	50 F (10-12 C)		60 F (16-18 C)		70 F (21 C)
March	**April**	**May**	**June**	**July**	

Wood Frog

Boreal Chorus Frog

Northern Leopard Frog

Plains Leopard Frog

American Toad

Northern Cricket Frog

Canadian Toad

Great Plains Toad

Cope's Gray Treefrog

Plains Spadefoot

Woodhouse's Toad

Gray Treefrog

Bullfrog

———— Dates with greatest abundance of calling frogs and toads in eastern South Dakota based on data collected since 1997.

Recommended listening period (with minumum water temperatures).

*Adapted from chorus chronology originally printed in Fischer et al. (1999)

Appendix E. Additional Snake Information

The text on snakebites and safety is reproduced by permission from South Dakota Department of Game, Fish and Parks. This text was originally included in Thompson and Backlund (1999).

Snakebite

What should you do if you or another person is bitten? First, briefly determine whether the snake is still in the area and if it is venomous, but do not waste time doing so. Any snake can bite, but in South Dakota only prairie rattlesnakes are venomous to people. If you see the snake, try to determine if it has rattles at the end of its tail. If a venomous snake bites someone, remain calm and seek medical attention immediately. Within the first 30 minutes you will know how serious the bite will be. It is best to transport the victim via vehicle to the nearest medical facility. In the meantime, a constricting band (e.g., Ace bandage) can be placed 2 to 4 inches above the bite (between the bite and the heart) to slow the movement of the venom into the circulatory and lymphatic systems. The area around the bite will swell up and turn black and blue, which can be very painful. Do not cut into the bite area, for this can potentially be more dangerous than the snakebite. Using ice, aspirin, or any alcohol on the bite is not recommended. While you are enroute to a medical facility, call them to facilitate preparation for the incoming snakebite patient.

Safety

Precautions for a person in snake country:

- *Learn how to identify venomous snakes.* Nonvenomous snakes in South Dakota have a pointed tail and round pupils. Prairie rattlesnakes are the only venomous snakes in South Dakota. Prairie rattlesnakes are born with a rattle segment – called a button – at the end of its tail, and adults have several rattle segments. They also have elliptical pupils and a triangular head. Nonvenomous snakes may also strike and bite if threatened.

- *Do not disturb, handle, or kill venomous snakes.* One third of the people bitten by snakes were attempting to capture, handle, or kill the snake. Any sudden movements can scare the snake, causing it to strike. If you do not bother the snake, it will not bother you.

- *Be careful where you place your hands and feet and where you sit.* Most snakes are sedentary animals that depend on concealment for protection. A rattlesnake can be difficult to see when it is motionless and silent. Also, most rattlesnakes will not rattle unless they are frightened or endangered, but do not depend on a rattlesnake to rattle before it strikes.

- *Do not jump over logs, rocks, or various plant materials.* Rattlesnakes often rest or search for food under these objects, so it is best to walk around them. When turning over rocks or logs, be wary of what might be underneath. When hiking, walk along paths and watch your step. Try to avoid tall grass or areas with heavy underbrush, so you can see your feet. Look closely at the ground before going over or under a fence.

- *Maintain a safe distance from a snake.* If you encounter or see a snake, maintain a distance from the snake of at least the length of its body. A snake can strike at least one half its body length, unless it is facing downhill. Snakes are not normally aggressive, but be prepared to retreat if it moves toward you. It may only be seeking escape cover.

- *Wear suitable clothing and footwear when outdoors.* Boots provide good protection for your feet and ankles, whereas sneakers and sandals do not. Rattlesnake fangs can penetrate clothing, however loose fitting clothes are better than tight fitting clothes.

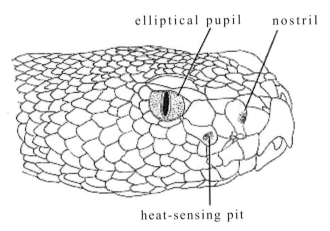

venomous snake

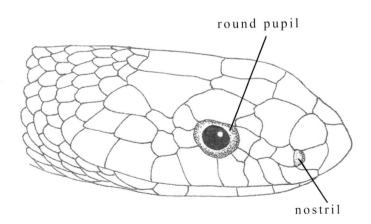

nonvenomous snake

Appendix F. South Dakota Frog and Toad CD Track List*

01. Introduction

02. American Toad - narration
03. American Toad - calls

04. Canadian Toad - narration
05. Canadian Toad - calls

06. Woodhouse's Toad - narration
07. Woodhouse's Toad - calls

08. Great Plains Toad - narration
09. Great Plains Toad - calls

10. Northern Cricket Frog - narration
11. Northern Cricket Frog - calls

12. Boreal Chorus Frog - narration
13. Boreal Chorus Frog - calls

14. Gray Treefrog - narration
15. Gray Treefrog - calls

16. Cope's Gray Treefrog - narration
17. Cope's Gray Treefrog - calls

18. Plains Spadefoot - narration
19. Plains Spadefoot - calls

20. Northern Leopard Frog - narration
21. Northern Leopard Frog - calls

22. Plains Leopard Frog - narration
23. Plains Leopard Frog - calls

24. Wood Frog - narration
25. Wood Frog - calls

26. Bullfrog - narration
27. Bullfrog - calls

28. Outro

*Narration and mixing by Lang Elliott, NatureSound Studio, www.musicofnature.com
Lang Elliott's email: langelliott@mac.com

All recordings of frog and toad calls © Lang Elliott, NatureSound Studio, www.musicofnature.com, except for Canadian Toad and second half of sound-print for Cope's Gray Treefrog, which are copyright Stan Tekiela: Author, Naturalist, and Wildlife Photographer